D1267808

Measure and the Integral

The Mathesis Series
Kenneth O. May, Editor

Counterexamples in Analysis
Bernard R. Gelbaum and John M. H. Olmsted

Measure and the Integral
Henri Lebesgue

Lectures on Calculus
Kenneth O. May

Evolution of Mathematical Thought
Herbert Meschkowski

Ways of Thought of Great Mathematicians
Herbert Meschkowski

Numbers and Ideals
Abraham Robinson

An Introduction to Sequences, Series, and Improper Integrals
O. E. Stanaitis

QA
312
.L43
1966

MEASURE AND THE INTEGRAL

by

Henri Lebesgue

Edited with a biographical essay by

Kenneth O. May

HOLDEN-DAY, INC.
San Francisco, London, Amsterdam
1966

147566

Copyright 1966 by Holden-Day, Inc., 728 Montgomery Street, San Francisco, California. All rights reserved. No part of this book may be reproduced in any form, by mimeograph or any other means, without permission in writing from the publisher.

Library of Congress Catalog Card Number: 66-26682
Printed in the United States of America

6/6/67

B v T

6.6.0

HENRI LEBESGUE
1875 - 1941

Photograph reproduced by permission of Gauthier-Villars, Paris.

EDITOR'S PREFACE

An English translation of *La Mesure des Grandeurs* is justified by the importance of the topic and the fame of the author. Contemporary theories of real numbers and of measure have in a sense made obsolete the Greek distinction between number and magnitude. But the problem of how to teach these modern ideas is very much alive. This book contains the mature judgments on this question of one of the greatest mathematical innovators of this century, who devoted a large part of his life to pedagogy.

On some matters Lebesgue's opinions do not coincide with current fashion or with this writer's views. So much the better! The important thing is his careful analysis of concepts in relation to learning, motivation, physical meaning, and rigor. Though written thirty years ago, and addressed to French teachers, his work is still relevant to mathematical education from the elementary grades through the university. It deserves to be read and pondered by every teacher of mathematics.

Sur le développement de la notion d'intégrale is a fine non-technical introduction to the modern theory of integration and that very rare thing, an informal account of a great idea by its originator. [For those who wish a systematic presentation, two classic treatments are now available in Dover paperback editions: H. Kestelman, *Modern Theories of Integration* (elementary) and Stanislaw Saks, *Theory of the Integral* (abstract and advanced).]

The translations have been made without revisions or modifications. Section titles, a few notes and bibliographic corrections have been added. Since there is no easily accessible account of Lebesgue's life, I have included a biographical sketch, selected bibliography, and portrait. I have benefitted from discussion with M. Loève and from comments of M. Frechet on a first draft of the biographical sketch, but for the opinions expressed I assume sole responsibility.

K. O. May

Berkeley, California
December, 1965.

CONTENTS

BIOGRAPHICAL SKETCH
OF HENRI LEBESGUE

by Kenneth O. May

The publication of mathematical "results" grows exponentially, but not the output of those profoundly simple and original contributions that open doors. Lebesgue's fame is based on his creation of one of the most fruitful mathematical concepts of the first half of the twentieth century.

Henri Lebesgue was born in Beauvais, fifty miles from Paris, on the 28th of June, 1875. His father was a typographical worker with a substantial library and serious intellectual interests. His mother was an elementary school teacher. The boy was soon noticed by his teachers, and local philanthropy enabled him to continue his education in spite of the early death of his father (18, p. 197).[1] In 1894 he entered the École Normale Supérieure, where he promptly showed his independence by ignoring those studies that did not interest him. In spite of coaching by Langevin, later one of France's great physicists, he managed to squeeze through the chemistry examination only by speaking rather softly to a somewhat deaf examiner and refusing to write on the blackboard (23, p. 14). More important for his future career, he began to question the statements of his professors. After hearing the theorem that a surface is applicable on the plane if and only if it is developable, he showed a crumpled handkerchief to his fellow students and announced that it must be a ruled surface since it was clearly applicable on a plane! (See 21, p. 584.)

[1] Numbers refer to references in the bibliography.

Such thoughtful irreverence led to his discoveries, but it earned him only a third place behind less able mathematicians when he graduated in 1897. While working for two years in the library of his alma mater he published his first four papers, which already clearly showed his turn of mind and contained his great ideas. The first (1) gave a simpler proof of the Weierstrass approximation theorem, whose existing proofs he thought "too clever." His third paper (2), based on the crumpled hand-kerchief, almost failed to be published because of the opposition of Hermite and others who were scandalized by functions without deriva-tives. Lebesgue soon felt the consequences of being an innovator, and was the target of facetious remarks about his supposed lack of interest in well behaved functions and surfaces (9, pp. 13–14).

In 1899 he went to the Lycée Central in Nancy. In spite of a heavy teaching load, he energetically continued his research. His doctoral thesis was accepted in 1902. Burkill (20, p. 58) says, "It cannot be doubted that this dissertation is one of the finest any mathematician has ever written." Of course, Lebesgue owed much to previous workers, and Borel's concept of the measure of a set was an essential prerequisite. But Lebesgue's definition of the integral was not "in the air" and might have remained undiscovered for another fifty years (21, p. 578). Picard wrote: "Riemann seemed to have investigated as deeply as possible the idea of the definite integral. Lebesgue showed that this was not at all the case." (See 17, p. 21.) Montel calls the Lebesgue integral "the principal algorithm created since Fourier series" (18, p. 198). Loève writes: ". . . the Archi-medes of the extension period was Henri Lebesgue. He took the decisive step in his thesis . . . In fact, contemporary theory of measure still dances to Lebesgue's tunes" (24). There have been many other tributes, but perhaps the best one in modern idiom was given casually by a col-league of mine recently. He remarked, "Once you have the Lebesgue integral, the sky's the limit."

Yet this great thesis was accepted for the degree only after some opposition, and its ideas continued to be criticised privately and in print. When Lebesgue took a copy of his thesis to Camille Jordan in 1902, the latter said to him, "Continue in scientific research, you will experience great joy from it. But you must learn to enjoy it alone. You will be a subject of astonishment to those close to you. You will not be much better understood by the scholarly world. Mathematicians have a place apart there, and even they do not always read each other" (11, pp. 91–92). Fortunately this estimate proved too pessimistic. Lebesgue's work was read and quickly valued by a few. He promptly moved to his first university appointment (Rennes) in 1902. He gave the Cours Peccot at the Collège de France on his new integral in the year 1902–1903 and on trigonometric series in 1904–1905, and these lectures were published in Borel's series of monographs (6 and 7). Though plagued by criticism and his own doubts, he wrote numerous papers exploiting his integral, and his fame grew as others applied his ideas and found them so remarkably fruitful. He moved to Poitiers in 1906 and to the Sorbonne in 1910. A series of prizes and other honors was crowned by his appointment to a professorship at the Collège de France in 1921 and to the Académie in 1922.

Though Lebesgue's ideas continued to become more dominant, more pervasive in analysis, Lebesgue the man did not have the influence that one might expect. He was not a political person—having interest neither in partisan politics outside the academic community nor in the gamesmanship required for academic power. He did what was expected in academic affairs and during World War I, but preferred to go his own way. He gathered few disciples or collaborators. He remained doubtful about the value of his own work ("un timide" in his own words, 13, p. x). He continued, as in his undergraduate days, to work on whatever happened to strike his fancy. Perhaps the very perfection of his thesis stunned both others and himself, and did not leave enough room for cooperative exploitation. In any case, others were stimulated to pick up the ball and run on their own. Before long Lebesgue was outside the mainstream of the development he had initiated, and the greatness of his original contribution overshadowed his continuing activity.

At the time of his election to the Academy Lebesgue had published nearly ninety books and papers on set theory, integration, area and arc length, measure theory, trigonometric series, polynomial approximation, calculus of variations (Plateau's problem and Dirichlet's problem), geometric probability, topology, and algebraic geometry (9, pp. 8–12). During the next twenty years he continued to write at about the same rate on topics which had interested him in the previous period, but now from an expository, philosophical, pedagogical and historical point of view. He also wrote on geometry and mechanics with the needs of teachers in mind. Besides conducting his lectures at the Collège de France, he taught at the two Écoles Normales Supérieures (rue d'Ulm and Sèvres) and gave generously of his time to assist individuals in their teaching and research.

As modern analysis continued to testify to the significance of his ideas, his fame and honors grew. His integral, which had been taught to undergraduates as early as 1914 by G. C. Evans at Rice Institute, became a basic ingredient of the curriculum in analysis. It was essential to the work of a host of mathematicians, most of whom hardly were aware that their benefactor was quietly continuing his work in Paris. In 1941, already touched by a terminal illness, he insisted on completing his course on geometrical constructions at the Collège de France, partly as a demonstration of his faith in liberation from the German occupation. From his bed he dictated a final book on conics. When he died in July 1941, he was survived by his mother, wife, a son and a daughter.

An index of Lebesgue's place in modern analysis is the list of entries under his name in the Naas-Schmid *Mathematisches Wörterbuch:* Lebesgue derivative basis, Lebesgue limit theorem, Lebesgue surface, Lebesgue function, Lebesgue integral, Lebesgue constant, Lebesgue criterion, Lebesgue curve, Lebesgue measure, Lebesgue algebra, Lebesgue-Nikodym theorem, Lebesgue sum, Lebesgue point, Lebesgue space, Lebesgue singularity, Lebesgue-Stieltjes integral, Lebesgue method of summation, and Lebesgue number. But these do not fully represent the man or his role.

Lebesgue was not a narrow specialist. He was a great student, innovator, and teacher. His ideas came from thoughtful questioning of the past. When one of his students, Lucienne Felix, asked him about his work in the history of mathematics, he replied, "I don't do history of science. I do science" (23, p. 11). He considered observation and study of previous work to be an essential part of scientific research. In the preface to the second edition of his *Lessons on Integration* (13), he wrote that "in order to do useful work it is necessary to march along paths opened by previous workers; acting otherwise, one runs too great a risk of creating a science without links with the rest of mathematics." In an article on Jordan (11, p. 97) he said that "the mathematician must carefully examine the domain in which he works, observe the role of the different mathematical entities which he meets, look at them live . . . in brief, the mathematician transforms himself into a naturalist." Montel says of him that "he excelled in looking at old things with new eyes. He knew the virtue of attentive examination of an example, of an anomaly, of an exception. He was suspicious of too general theories whose formalism and verbalism repelled him. He had a geometric vision of mathematical facts and preferred synthetic insights which satisfy and nourish the mind to analytic proofs which reassure it" (18, p. 199).

Lebesgue himself wrote that "reduced to general theories, mathematics would be a beautiful form without content. It would die quickly, as many branches of our science have died just at the time when general results seemed to guarantee them a new activity; I cite, as examples, the theory of forms, and elliptic functions—so completely ignored since Weierstrass presented the general theorems about them. General theories reply to the questions that are asked of them. Unfortunately, they reply too easily without requiring of us any effort, and since they give us the solution of problems before we have studied them, they weaken our curiosity and deny us the intimate knowledge which would have led to new problems. They even make people disdainful of particular researches from which might come these new problems, because such particular researches cannot have the same elegance as general theories" (10, pp. 192–193).

Lebesgue's ideas on teaching were as distinctive and firmly held as those on the nature of mathematical research. He believed that living mathematics should be presented to the student in a genetic style. This meant using the history of ideas to explain mathematical concepts. It meant trying to present things simply, not in order to falsify but to strip away inessentials. His conception of the lecturer's role was summed up neatly in his own words: "The only instruction which a professor can give, in my opinion, is to think in front of his students" (23, p. 8). In order to accomplish this he believed that the teacher should constantly enrich his own mathematical culture and at the same time refuse to remember his own lectures and the routines of previous pedagogues and textbooks. According to Lucienne Felix, this is what Lebesgue meant when he said he refused to "know" the mathematics he taught. He believed that students "gain nothing from a solution that is satisfying from the logical, but not from the human point of view" (23, p. 9).

In a brief sketch it is not possible to include further evidence, but it is clear that Lebesgue should not be remembered as a specialist, nor as an innovator who abandoned research for teaching. On the contrary, he was from beginning to end a thoughtful analyst of mathematical ideas in relation to history and teaching. This approach led him to one epoch-making creation, to numerous valuable results, and to a lifetime of useful work as a teacher and expositor.

SELECTED BIBLIOGRAPHY

(Only volume number and year are given, since the articles are easily located within a volume.)

Works by Lebesgue

1. "Sur l'approximation des fonctions," *Bulletin des Sciences Mathématiques*, **22**, 1898. (His first paper; a simpler proof of the Weierstrass theorem.)
2. "Sur quelques surfaces non réglées applicables sur le plan," *Comptes rendus de l'Académie des Sciences*, **128**, 1899. (The crumpled handkerchief.)
3. "Sur une généralisation de l'intégrale définie," *Comptes rendus*, **132**, 1900. (Definition of the Lebesgue integral!)
4. "Intégrale, Longueur, Aire," thesis. Published separately in Paris and in *Annali de Matematica*, Ser. 3, **7**, 1902.
5. "Sur l'existence des dérivées," *Comptes rendus*, **136**, 1903. (The derivative of the definite integral equals the integrand almost everywhere.)
6. *Leçons sur l'intégration et la recherche des fonctions primitives*, Paris, 1904. (Ninety-eight out of 138 pages devoted to history.)
7. *Leçons sur les séries trigonométriques*, Paris, 1906.
8. "Sur les programmes d'arithmétique et d'algèbre," *Revue de l'Enseignement des Sciences*, 1910. (His first paper on pedagogy as such, though he had previously published in this journal in 1909 and in *Enseignement mathématique* in 1908.)
9. *Notice sur les travaux scientifiques de M. Henri Lebesgue*, Toulouse, 1922. (The scientific autobiography required of candidates to the Académie. It includes a complete bibliography up to that time.)
10. "Humbert et Jordan, Roberval et Ramus," *Enseignement mathématique*, Ser. 2, **3**, 1957. (Originally published in *Revue scientifique*, **60**, 1922.)
11. "Notice sur la vie et les travaux de Camille Jordan," *Enseignement mathématique*, Ser. 2, **3**, 1957. (Originally read before the Academy in 1923.)
12. "Sur le développement de la notion d'intégrale," *Matematisk Tidsskrift*, Copenhagen, 1926. (Reprinted in *Revue de Metaphysique et de Morale*, **34**, 1927 and in Spanish in *Revista Matematica Hispano-Americana*, Ser. 2, **2**, 1927, and in English in this volume.)

13. *Leçons sur l'intégration*, Paris, 1928. (Second edition of number 6, this bibliography, with important additions.)
14. "Sur la mesure des grandeurs," *Enseignement mathématique*, **31–34,** 1933–1936. (Later reprinted by the magazine as a separate monograph and here in English translation.)
15. *Les Coniques*, Paris, 1942.
16. *Leçons sur les Constructions géométriques*, Paris, 1950.

References on Lebesgue

17. E. Picard, *Les sciences mathématiques en Frances depuis un demi-siècle*, Paris, 1917.
18. P. Montel, "Notice nécrologique sur M. Henri Lebesgue," *Comptes rendus*, **213**, 1941.
19. H. Fehr, "Henri Lebesgue," *Enseignement mathématique*, **38,** 1942.
20. J. C. Burkill, "Henri Lebesgue," *Journal of the London Mathematical Society*, **19,** 1944.
21. A. Denjoy, "Notice sur la vie et l'oeuvre de Henri Lebesgue," *Notices et Discours de l'Académie des Sciences*, **2** (1937–1948), Paris, 1949.
22. L. Felix, "Quelques aspects de l'histoire des mathématiques . . ." *Revue Générale des Sciences Pures et Appliquées*, **60,** 1953.
23. A. Denjoy, L. Felix, and P. Montel, "Henri Lebesgue, le savant, le professeur, l'homme," *Enseignement mathématique*, 1957. (Includes an account of the polemic between Lebesgue and Borel.)
24. M. Loève, "Integration and Measure," *Encyclopaedia Britannica*, 1965.

Part I

MEASURE OF MAGNITUDES

Measure of Magnitudes is a translation by Scripta Technica of LA MESURE DES GRANDEURS, originally published serially in *l'Enseignement Mathématique* (1931–1935) and reprinted as the first of the MONOGRAPHIES DE L'ENSEIGNEMENT MATHEMATIQUE.

INTRODUCTION

I thank Professor H. Fehr for accepting in his review articles of a more elementary nature than one ordinarily finds in that publication. The only justification for their acceptance is the fact that they deal with questions on the teaching of mathematics. I am all the more obliged because these articles are quite long for the slight amount of scientific information they contain. They are concerned not so much with facts as with opinions; to avoid misunderstandings, it was necessary to present arguments supporting these opinions. The idea of writing these articles came to me as follows.

Since 1910, I have served on the staff of one École normale supérieure or the other, devoted to preparing young people of both sexes for teaching at the secondary level. Part of the program of instruction is composed of lessons dealing with the secondary curriculum. Thus I have had an opportunity to think a great deal about such programs and to observe the obstacles that most frequently cause young teachers to stumble. I have been struck by how often certain good and bad qualities occur. I have also had an opportunity to examine textbooks and to learn about present-day tendencies in the teaching profession from them and from the reports of boards of examiners. Furthermore, since I have been in a position to evaluate the results of teaching in the thirty years that I have been giving entrance and baccalaureate examinations, it is not at all surprising that the idea should occur to me of writing articles in a pedagogical vein—if I may use an expression which usually puts mathematicians to flight.

In these pages I shall deal with the measure of quantities. There is no more fundamental subject than this. Measure is the starting point of all mathematical applications, and since applied mathematics obviously preceded pure mathematics (mathematical logic), it is usually supposed that geometry originated in the measure of areas and volumes. Furthermore, measure provides us with numbers, the very subject of analysis. Therefore, we discuss the measure of quantities at all three levels of teaching: primary, secondary, and higher. The study of what is done at all three teaching levels furnishes us with an example of an effort to coordinate and to comprehend the whole, which, it seems to me, would contribute more effectively to the training of future teachers than the work that is now required of them—verbal refinement of isolated lessons.

In the chapters that follow, the reader will see that I have endeavored to deal with the questions involved in as simple and specific a manner as possible but without sacrificing logical rigor. This ideal may seem somewhat archaic in an age in which learned, abstract considerations play a dominant role, even in the experimental sciences. But those whom we have to thank for such abstract considerations have been able to think in abstractions and at the same time to perform useful work precisely because they had a particularly acute sense of reality. It is this sense of reality that we must strive to waken in the young. Afterwards, but only then, will the passage to abstraction prove profitable. Then one will be able to see the concrete in the abstract and all the truly useful cases in the general.

In two chapters, which are in a way preliminary, I deal with whole numbers and then with numbers required for the measure of quantities. After this, having arrived at my subject, I deal with areas, volumes, and quantities in general.

I
COMPARISON OF COLLECTIONS. WHOLE NUMBERS

1 *Counting.* If a very small child is asked to take a piece of candy for himself and to give a piece to his two sisters, he will first secure his own share and will then take a piece to one of his sisters and will return to fetch another piece to take to the other sister. When he is somewhat older, he will take certain shortcuts; he will take three pieces of candy, saying, "For me, for Louise, for Renée."

We can easily imagine (and studies made among certain primitive peoples seem to confirm this hypothesis) that by an analogous mechanism the need to compare two collections led man to *counting*, that is, the comparison of two collections with a single standard collection—the collection of the words in a certain phrase. These words are called *numbers*. To count or to number, we mentally attach a different object of the collection to each of these successive words of the phrase (or sequence) of numbers. The last number pronounced is the number of the collection.

This number is viewed as the result of the experimental operation of numbering since it is a complete report of it. An experimental result allows us to dispense with other experiments: The rules for the four operations relieve us of performing counting operations for certain collections that can be formed from collections already numbered.

On the basis of these rules we may state various facts that are usually set forth as theorems, although the supposed proofs are in reality only experimental verifications. An example is the theorem that a product is independent of the order of the factors. These rules all spring from the general observation that the number associated with a collection does not depend on the order in which the members of the collection are arranged for counting.

2 *Numbers and metaphysics.*   It may perhaps be worthwhile to emphasize the points in which the present exposition differs from those that may be found in arithmetic treatises.[1] I open one by J. Tannery. Indeed, this work does describe the operation of numbering a collection and I read proofs that amount to experimental descriptions. However, it appears that an experimental number is only a utilization here, an application of a metaphysical entity of which the second paragraph of the book gives us a sort of definition: "The concept of a whole number results, by abstraction, from the concept of a collection of distinct objects. It is independent of the nature of the objects. . . ." We often say "independent of the nature and order of the objects."

Thus, numbers are presented as quite mysterious things, but most frequently, one hastens to add that nothing is clearer or simpler. P. Boutroux in paragraph two of his *Principes de l'Analyse mathématique* writes: "The origin and logical meaning of the concept of number have been much discussed and will continue to be discussed for a long time. Fortunately, this concept is among those that need no definitions and commentaries. Since that remote age in which man learned to count, number has become one of the fundamental ideas that engage our thought —an idea so immediate and so clear to the understanding that in trying to analyze it, we at first succeed only in obscuring it. This is why arithmetic could be built on incomplete verbal definitions and be nonetheless considered at all times as the perfect science *par excellence*."

In my opinion, the fact that it was possible to construct arithmetic can be more clearly explained than by saying, with P. Boutroux, that it is inexplicable. We have a complete definition of number: the description of the operation that gives us number. To this experimental definition men have seen fit to add a mystique and metaphysics. Teaching no longer deals with a mystique. It takes a neutral position, leaving any one free to view the number 13, for instance, as favorable or ominous. However, out of tradition, respect, or fear of being considered elementary, teaching makes a great ado of metaphysics. Only it does not use it, and this is why it makes little difference to the success of arithmetic that the metaphysical notions are obscure. Having said this, I pay my respects

---

[1] I do not mention the fact that, in these expositions, numbers appear first in their cardinal sense, whereas I begin with ordinal numbers. A number becomes cardinal only at the instant at which we declare the result obtained to be independent of the order in which the objects are counted.

to metaphysics, but since it would require leisure and since what we have before us is work, I remain neutral and I consider arithmetic to be experimental science just like the others.

3 *Applicability of arithmetic.*   But what becomes of "mathematical certainty," which at all times has occupied the attention of philosophers, if there is no longer anything but "applied mathematics?" It degenerates and is now only the least precarious of our certainties. Arithmetic, which man in his aspirations toward the absolute has made "the perfect science *par excellence*," is now only the least imperfect of our sciences. It is the humanly perfect science that in practice never deceives us. Whence comes such superiority?

First of all, why is it that we are so often wrong when we try to apply an experimental result? The answer is that the limits of such a result are never well known. When we say that if a glass rod is rubbed, it will attract small pieces of paper, this implies the fulfillment of quite a few implicit and ill-defined conditions. We ought to be able to define what we mean by "glass," "paper," and "rub," and to precisely indicate the time, distances, masses, atmospheric conditions, etc.

Arithmetic, as such, uses only a very small number of empirical observations, each one of which has been repeated many times over by every human being ever since there have been humans. Thus, we know without hesitation in what cases arithmetic is applicable and in what cases it is not applicable. In the latter cases, the thought of applying arithmetic does not even occur to us. We think of applying arithmetic only when it is applicable, so much so that we forget that there are cases in which it is not applicable. For example, we say that two and two make four. Suppose that I pour two liquids into one glass and two liquids into another glass; then I pour all of this into a vase. Will it contain four liquids? You may say that this is a trick and not a question of arithmetic.

Suppose I put two animals in a cage and then two more. How many animals will the cage then contain? Will you say that my lack of seriousness is even more apparent now and that it depends on the species of the animals since one of them may eat the others? You would also like to know whether the counting of the animals is done immediately or one year later, as by then some of the animals may die or have young. In short, you do not know whether the collections of which I am speaking are immutable or not, whether each object in a collection retains its individuality, or whether any objects may appear or disappear. What does this mean but that certain conditions must be satisfied for arithmetic to be applicable? As to the rule that you have just given me for determining whether it is applicable or not, it is certainly excellent from a practical experimental point of view, but it has no logical value. It is the recognition that arithmetic is applicable when it is applicable. And this is why we cannot prove that two and two make four, which nonetheless is an excellent example of a truthful statement since we never go wrong in using it.

In purely logical expositions, where arithmetic deals with symbols void of any meaning, it is only by virtue of an axiom that two and two make four. I shall not speak here about expositions of this sort, but may I state that granting their considerable mathematical importance and the fact that they have taught us much, it seems to me, nevertheless, that they are doomed to complete failure if we take them to clarify the notion of a number without recourse to experience. In these logical games, we do, in fact, handle collections of symbols (whether actual or imagined is of slight importance), and it is then that all our knowledge acquired from experience with regard to these collections, that is, with regard to numbers, intervenes.

4 *Rigor in arithmetic.* Philosophy has weighed so heavily on the teaching of mathematics that I felt that to avoid misunderstandings, I should give these explanations, which have diverted me from my purely pedagogical goal. I return to it, remarking that the usual recommendation that, "One must not confuse a number with the symbol that represents it," has no meaning for us. As soon as it is explained just what counting is, it would be appropriate to give the sequence of numbers, that is, to explain the decimal system of numeration.[1] It matters little that there are other ways of naming numbers. This should not hinder us any more than the fact that words are different in English and French, which is no problem since we may translate from one language into the other, although there the correspondence is not entirely definite. The correspondence between one system of numeration and another, however, is absolutely precise. There is no disadvantage in using any one of them. What does it matter that man might have adopted the numbering system with base 11, had

---

[1] And this can be done without use of the theorems on numbers. It should also be noted that all peoples who have the concept of number use a more or less rudimentary decimal system.

he eleven fingers? *We have a unique opportunity to have a universal language at our disposal, namely, the written decimal system of numeration; let us use it.*

In short, I propose that we use in the upper classes of our secondary education the same procedures as in the lower classes and at the primary level, procedures that at the present time people feel obliged to denounce and scorn. Among other advantages, this would enable students to understand clearly that the only purpose of the study of arithmetic at the close of their secondary education is to elucidate completely, to arrive at a clear formulation, and a conscious grasp of what up to then had been felt unconsciously and without analysis. At the present time, the only ones who understand it are a few very gifted minds, really abnormal cases in no need of either support or guidance and about whom teachers need not be concerned. To the other students, this re-examination of arithmetic is a completely new thing, something that one learns for the examination and that sometimes has only a vague relationship with actual calculations.

5 *Numbers and numerals.*   What could be objected to the type of exposition suggested here? First of all, our metaphysical habits. "Is it not blasphemy to call the number a symbol since numbers once constituted the very essence of things?" Here we have fear manifesting itself in the most varied forms. For instance, let us say that we may certainly use interchangeably the English word *chair* or the French word *chaise* because they both refer to the same object, but what is the analogue of the object chair in the use of the symbols 101 in the binary system and 5 in the decimal system? Since there is no chair hidden under 5, we can avoid the difficulty by a verbal pirouette and speak of the metaphysical entity 5, which will replace the physical reality chair. This amounts to refusing to answer the question.

In answer, it should be pointed out that from one language to another word-for-word translation only applies to substantives with concrete meanings. Apart from those, translations are made sentence by sentence. It is not the word number that we need to explain but rather the sentences in which that word appears. For instance, consider the following sentences: Two collections have the same number; two collections do not have the same number. Now, this is precisely what was explained at the outset in describing the operation of numbering a collection. Thus, we remove any reason for metaphysical fears.

A description of numbering has shown that the choice of the sequence of numbers (words or symbols) was of accessory theoretical importance. It is only a matter of choosing one of all the existing or conceivable languages. But we cannot express ourselves without choosing some language.

In secondary education, where one of the goals, if not the most important one, is the legitimation of the rules of calculation, I propose that we choose the decimal system from the very beginning. At an advanced level, where one no longer is concerned with actual calculations, this choice would be a poor one because there the study of arithmetic leads to various generalizations of the operations, but not of the decimal system of numeration itself, which has never been imitated. There, we would accept temporary numerations such as those that are utilized when we say, for example, "suppose that a, b, and c are three numbers and d is the product of a and the quotient of b divided by c. . . ."

If I constantly use the decimal system in secondary teaching, it is for simple pedagogical reasons. Time is saved in so doing and a number written according to the decimal system is a concrete thing about which young minds reason more easily. It is, however, not my intention at all to exaggerate the importance of this system.[1] And, if I were addressing pupils who have just finished their secondary schooling, I would willingly, without feeling that I was going back on my stated views, adopt a more abstract presentation: Numbers are symbols for which two types of composition have been developed, namely, addition and multiplication.[2]

6 *The decimal system.* I apologize for dwelling so long on whole numbers. However, this gives me an opportunity to explain thoroughly my attitude toward metaphysics—which I am trying to separate from teaching to the limited degree permitted by our language and all our thinking habits, leaving any one free to add metaphysics and mysticism to the education he has received—and to explain the constant use that I shall make of the decimal system.

This constant use appears so natural and pedagogically desirable to me, that it may be more appropriate to ask why the decimal system is

---

[1] For example, see section IV of the final note to the second edition of my *Leçons sur l'Intégration.*

[2] With regard to this statement, I will point out that if it is a blasphemy to reduce a number from the rank of an entity to the rank of a symbol, *it is a blasphemy that all mathematicians commit.* The exposition I am advocating, therefore, should not be singled out for such a charge.

ordinarily used so little. Primarily, the reason is that the Greeks, our models, did not use it. They were unable to do so both because of metaphysics and especially because they had only an imperfect numeration, one that was akin to our decimal system but very limited. It was so limited that Archimedes needed to extend it considerably for the calculations in his extraordinary work on the grains of sand, where we see clearly that the absence of an unlimited numbering system was a serious obstacle to understanding the exact content of the concept of a number.

The decimal notation is not a heritage from the Greeks. As a result, everything dealing with that notation has been superimposed on Greek teaching and not incorporated into it. *Our teaching does not yet make full use of that historic event, which is perhaps the most important event in the history of science, namely, the invention of the decimal system of numeration.*

II

LENGTHS. NUMBERS

7 *From whole numbers to numbers in general.*   I shall again start with a brief résumé of an exposition. I chose it in accordance with the traditional manner of presenting geometry in which motions are used to explore space. This manner is certainly the one that deviates the least from the steps that our ancestors must have taken to master the experimental truths that form the base of geometry.

In this exposition, having pointed out the needs that may have led men to compare distances and to define what they meant by equal or unequal distances, I would describe the process of comparison, let us say, of a segment AB with a segment U, known as a unit segment. Let us lay off U on the half-line AB, first from A to $A\alpha$, then on $\alpha\beta$, etc. Suppose that A_1 is the last point that can be reached in this manner without passing point B. If we can reach A by laying U off three times, we say that the length of AB (in terms of the unit length U) is 3 if A_1 is at point B. Otherwise, we say that the length of AB is greater than 3 but less than 4. This means that B is always one of the points of the segment A_1B_1 that starts at A_1 and is equal to U, but that it is never the point B_1.

Let us divide U into ten equal parts (that is, let us take a segment U_1 in terms of which the measure of U is 10),[1] and let us repeat these operations. We shall arrive at a segment A_2B_2 contained in A_1B_1. The length of AA_2 in terms of the unit length U_1 will be between 30 and 39. Suppose, for example, that it is 37. The length of AB in terms of the unit length U_1 is then said to be at least equal to 37 but less than 38.

If in the same manner we turn from U_1 to a segment U_2, we shall obtain figures like 376 and 377, for example, then, 3760 and 3761, then, 37602 and 37603, etc.

Now, we need to imagine *a symbol which we call a number and regard as the complete report or result of this unlimited sequence of operations.*

---

[1] Regarding the existence of U_1, see the footnote to section 21.

length, the length of U_{i-1} is 5, and that of U is $5 \times 10^{i-1}$. Thus, the approximating values that we have found approach each other arbitrarily closely.

Operations

Just as with integers, operations performed on numbers eliminate certain experiments since they make it possible to deduce what the result of these experiments would be by using the results of previous experiments.

9 *Addition.*   We know what we mean by a segment that is the sum of two other segments. Let us now seek to find the length of the sum of two segments whose individual lengths we already know. Let AB be the sum of the segments $A\omega$ and ωB. Let (AB), (ωA), and (ωB) be the three lengths. To evaluate (AB), we start with the point ω as was just described. The segment $a_i\omega$ contains U_i an integral number of times. The number $(\omega A)_i$ is the one that we derive from (ωA) by omitting in the latter number both the decimal point and the digits beyond the ith digit. Similarly with ωb_i. Thus, $a_i b_i$ contains U_i $d_i = (\omega A)_i + (\omega B)_i$ times and $a_i' b_i'$ contains U_i $e_i = (\omega A)_i + (\omega B)_i + 2$ times. Thus, the length of $a_i b_i$ and $a_i' b_i'$ (with U taken as unit length) are numbers that can be obtained by setting off by decimal points i digits to the right of d_i and e_i.

From this, we get the rule giving (AB), that is, the rule for adding two numbers, in particular, two decimal numbers.

With regard to the properties of addition, let us note only that expressed by the equality $x + y = y + x$. It can be deduced either from the geometrical definition or from the rule for making the calculation.

10 *Multiplication.*[1]   Suppose that we know the length, let us say 37.425 . . . , of a segment AB in terms of a unit length U and that we know the length of U in terms of a unit length V, let us say 4.632 . . . . What is the length of AB in terms of the unit V?

---

[1] Multiplication of integers is assumed to have been defined in terms analogous to those to be described. Every question involving multiplication is a problem of change of unit or of objects: 5 sacks containing 300 apples each, 2.75 meters of material at 28.45 francs per meter.

We note that 4.632 . . . is also the length of the segment V_i contained 10^i times in V in terms of the unit U_i contained 10^i times in U.

Now, AB contains the segment U_2 3742 times and is in turn contained in a segment made up of 3743 lengths each equal to U_2. The segment U_2 itself contains 463 segments of length V_4 and is in turn contained in a segment made up of 464 such segments. Thus, AB contains a segment AB_2 made up of V_4 laid out 3742 × 463 times and is contained in a segment AB_2' made up of V_4 laid out 3743 × 464 times. Since we know the lengths of AB_2 and AB_2' in terms of the unit V_4, the lengths in terms of the unit V can be obtained by shifting the decimal four digits to the right. Thus we have approximate values (below and above) for the length of AB in terms of the unit length V.

It remains to show that this method yields values arbitrarily close to each other. Now, according to the principles of multiplication of integers, the segment B_2B_2' contains 3742 + 463 + 1 segments equal to V_4; that is, the length in terms of the unit V_2 is

$$37.42 + 4.63 + 0.01 < 37.425\cdots + 4.632\cdots + 0.01.$$

Therefore, it is less than

$$N = (37 + 1) + (4 + 1) + 1.$$

Similarly, if we use the first three digits of the two given numbers, we would be led to an interval B_3B_3' whose length in terms of the unit V_3 would be less than this number N, etc.

Whatever this number N may be, there is an integral power of 10, let us say 10^h, that is greater than N. Here, $h = 2$. Therefore, since B_iB_i' contains fewer than N segments V_i, it contains a fortiori fewer than 10^h such segments. In other words, for $i > h$, V contains more than 10^{i-h} segments equal to B_iB_i', and the approximating values found for the length of AB in terms of the unit V become arbitrarily close to each other.

Hence the rule: The successive digits of the desired number, known as the product of the two given numbers, are the same as the digits (in the corresponding positions) of the number obtained for sufficiently large values of i by dropping from both given numbers the decimal point and the digits beyond the ith digit, by increasing each of the two integers thus obtained by one unit, by taking the product of the integers thus increased, and finally by setting off by a decimal point $2i$ digits at the right of that product.[1]

---

[1] May I remind you that this exposition is addressed to teachers. For the precautions to be taken for students, see section 17.

The properties of multiplication reduce essentially to those expressed by the equalities $xy = yx$ and $(x + y)z = xz + yz$. They are immediately derived from the preceding rule. Furthermore, the second of them is perhaps an immediate result of the geometrical definition of multiplication, although this is not true of the first.

Naturally, we set $x \times 0 = 0 \times x = 0$.

11 *Subtraction and division.*   These operations can be defined either geometrically (which has the advantage of showing immediately that they are possible for $a - b$ if $b < a$ and for a/b if $b \neq 0$ and that there is only one solution) or algebraically (as inverse operations). We shall arrive at the rule giving the successive digits of the result. These rules are completely analogous to those giving the digits of a sum or product but this time they use, instead of two approximate values exceeding the correct value, an approximate value greater than a and an approximate value less than b.

With regard to the properties of subtraction and division, we may confine ourselves to the one expressing the equality $a \times \dfrac{b}{c} = \dfrac{ab}{c}$, from which we derive

$$\frac{a}{\dfrac{c}{b}} = \frac{ab}{c} \quad \text{and} \quad \frac{\dfrac{c}{a}}{b} = \frac{c}{ab}.$$

Let us represent by S_T the length of a segment S in terms of the unit T. We determine successively T, U, and S beginning with V and a, b, and c by

$$a = S_U, \quad b = U_V, \quad c = T_V;$$

$$S_T = S_U \times U_T = S_U + \frac{U_V}{T_V} = a \times \frac{b}{c}$$

and

$$S_T = \frac{S_V}{T_V} = \frac{S_U \times U_V}{T_V} = \frac{ab}{c},$$

which proves the equality above.

Rules of calculations with all numbers are thus made quite legitimate. Those dealing with terminating decimals or with fractions are particular cases of the more general rules.

12 *Independence of the unit.*   Before determining precisely the import of this observation, I wish to say that the exposition that I have just sketched should include the following fundamental remark:

A number has no concrete meaning unless the unit segment U is fixed. Then, the number is the result of comparison with U of a segment whose length we may reconstruct beginning with the given number. From this it is not at all obvious a priori that if, of two numbers x and y, the greater in terms of the unit U is x, x would also be the greater in terms of any other unit, or that if certain numbers z_1, z_2, . . . , z'_1, z'_2 . . . form two sequences of values that approach arbitrarily close to a number z in terms of the unit U, the same would be true with any other unit, or that if the relation $u = s + t$ is true with one unit U, it would also be true with any other unit. It is only because comparison of the digits of x and y make it possible to see which is greater, because the digits belonging to z are determined by those of z_i and z'_i, and because the digits in s and in t determine those of u, that all these facts are independent of the choice of U and we may speak, for example, of *the product of two numbers* and not just of *the product of two numbers when the unit is U.*

Therefore, we may deal with operations on numbers without needing to refer to any one specific concrete utilization of these numbers.

This supremely important fact, which forms the base of analysis, is related to the following geometrical fact: If there exists a homogeneous relation between the lengths of several segments with respect to the unit U, this relation remains between the lengths with respect to any other unit. It is from this that we get what may be called the homogeneity of the formulas for one-dimensional geometry. I confine myself to this observation because the matter does not bear on my subject, to which I now return with a discussion of the proposed mode of exposition.

13 *Pedagogical critique.*   Some of my readers will say, "But this is what we always do!" I shall shortly agree and I shall base my stand on the fact that this is in effect what one does in practice all the time; but, in theory, one has quite different pretensions and, from that point of view, the above exposition is decidedly revolutionary. For example, here is what is done in the French curriculum, which is only slightly different in this respect from those of other countries.

At the primary level, and in the first classes of the secondary level, we teach children what numbers are, without learned or pretentious definitions, by having them work with numbers—first, the one-digit numbers, then the two-digit numbers, and finally whole numbers in general. For example, by means of the metric system, they learn the use of the decimal point and they become accustomed to working with decimals. At this stage of teaching, numbers are indeed reports of experiences in numbering or measuring of which I have spoken above. At no time are they led into metaphysics.

Also, we teach the pupils to work with fractions. Whether from working with fractions or from performing such divisions as that of 1 by 3 or from the extraction of square roots, the children encounter numbers that can be written in decimal form only by means of an infinite sequence of digits. We certainly avoid bringing this fact too much to their attention, or telling them that it is frightening and disconcerting—and the children are neither frightened nor disconcerted.

Thus, we admit in the course of teaching at these levels that the concept of a number is acquired and that we may speak of operations on any numbers whatsoever. We then come to the square of the hypotenuse and calculate the diagonal $a\sqrt{2}$ of a square in geometry, and in algebra we introduce the rules pertaining to the signs that occur in the operations,[1] but it is assumed that the operations on positive numbers are known.

Thus, one goes to the first part of the baccalaureate, up to the end of the first grade,[*] using somewhat imprecise notions of purely experimental origin. In the following class, however, the mathematics program, which is reserved for students wishing to push their scientific learning further, the student will revise his ideas and he will be given a more solid base. My criticisms and observations bear only on the expositions that are given at that time.

---

[1] I may remark in passing that if we define the operations on positive and negative numbers as we have just done for numbers, replacing the use of undirected segments with the use of vectors, the rules regarding the signs lose all artificial character.

[*] Translator's note: A comment on the French educational system may make the author's remarks here and elsewhere in the book more intelligible to the reader. The French Lycée (roughly equivalent to our high school and possibly the first year or so of college) consists of seven grades, the first six of which are numbered in decreasing order (that is, the sixth grade is the lowest). In the last year, the instruction is divided into two branches, one for the pupils interested in the humanities, the other for those interested in the natural sciences. The full title of the latter branch is "Classe de Mathématiques Élémentaires"; it is referred to in this book as "the mathematics program" or "the last year."

The expression "instruction at the secondary level," which occurs repeatedly in this book, refers to Lycée instruction.

14 *Deceptions.* In the mathematics program of the last year, we take up the concept of an integer, then that of a fraction, then that of a terminating decimal treated as a particular type of fraction. The definitions of the operations, which were suggested by experience, are put in a purely logical fashion. All of this is logically coherent and I only need to repeat this remark, which in a way has already been made: If it is only a matter of justifying the methods of calculating with integers and decimals, we are making a very long detour and one with the pedagogical inconvenience of being too different in form from the earlier teaching for the students to understand clearly that it is simply a matter of clarifying definitively what they have already known since elementary school. However, my chief criticism has to do with what is said, or rather with what is not said, with regard to irrational numbers.

In the final (just as in the initial) class of secondary instruction, irrational numbers are spoken of in a manner only to avoid discussing them. What is already clear in the mind is gone over again in order to teach the students to formulate it in words. No attempt is made to define the rational and irrational numbers, which have remained more than vague, while serving well for the past four years without every having been explicitly discussed. These numbers are encountered everywhere, and everywhere one avoids speaking of them clearly. In arithmetic, when we measure quantities, we deal with a comparison of lengths, but we do not go beyond the commensurable cases. The other cases are omitted or evaded with varying skill. Also, we resign ourselves to a veritable game of legerdemain with regard to approximating values. We can speak only of approximating values of rational numbers since it is only of rational numbers that we have been speaking. Now, these approximating values are infinitely less interesting for rational numbers than for the remaining numbers. But, in a way, these other numbers do not exist. It is quite simple, *we proceed to speak of approximating numbers that do not approximate anything.*

Let me recall for you how this comes about. First, two meanings of the expression "approximating value" are confounded, which is not too serious but very useful here. In all the rest of mathematics, *lower approximating value* within an ϵ distance means a value less than the number ξ but differing from that number ξ by at most ϵ. Here, lower approximating value within $1/10$ denotes the greatest integral number of tenths not exceeding the precise number. Now, for this introduction to arithmetic, the precise number ξ is always in actuality a root of a simple algebraic equation $f(\xi) = 0$, and one may define the approximating value $x/10$ within $1/10$ of the number by a difference of sign between $f(x/10)$ and $f((x + 1)/10)$, without speaking of ξ. One may thus say:

The quotient of A divided by B is, within $1/10$ below A/B, the fraction $x/10$, if x is the greatest integer such that $10A - Bx$ is positive or zero.

The square root of A, within $1/10$ below the square root, is $x/10$, where x is the greatest integer such that $10^2 A - x^2$ is positive or zero.

Note carefully the enormous difference between these two cases. In the first case, the number ξ exists; I mean that it is rational and that we have the right to speak of it. In the second case, it does not exist. In the first case, $x/10$ is a lower approximating value within $1/10$ (in the general mathematical sense of the words—approximating values) of the exact quotient, ξ, of A divided by B. In the second case, $x/10$ is not the approximating value of $\sqrt{A}$ since the latter does not exist. How can we expect the students not to make analogous grammatical transformations in the two cases—transformations that are permissible in one case but not in the other?

Furthermore, if the number $x/10$ were not an approximating value of ξ, it would serve no purpose except being defined. The square root of 2 (within $1/10$ below) does serve because, for example, it is what we obtain at the second stage of measuring the diagonal of the square constructed on the unit length. It is therefore *indispensible* that the students make the transformation or, if you prefer, the grammatical confusion that one has pretended to avoid by taking certain language precautions: Quotient within $1/10$ and square root within $1/10$ rather than approximating values within $1/10$ of the quotient or the root.

This is a real hypocrisy, quite frequent in the teaching of mathematics. The teacher takes verbal precautions, which are valid in the sense that he gives to them, but that the students *most assuredly* will not understand in the same way. Unfortunately, competitive examinations often encourage one to commit this little bit of deception. The teachers must train their students to answer little fragmentary questions well, and they give them model answers that are often veritable masterpieces and that leave no room for criticism. To achieve this, the teachers isolate each question from the whole of mathematics and create for this question alone a perfect language without bothering with its relationships to other questions. Mathematics is no longer a monument but a heap. I insist on this point although it is perfectly well known to all teachers, who will say with irony, "Fashion dictates precision at one point in the course and all sorts of liberties at another." The good students have seen enough to be skeptical, too, instead of enthusiastic. An infinite amount of talent has been expended on little perfections of detail. We must now attempt an overhaul of the whole structure.

Thus, in the mathematics program of the last year, calculations within 1/10 of some number would seem to make inevitable the definition of a number as a sequence of digits, and yet, neither this definition nor any other is given. The issue is avoided, sometimes by various kinds of subterfuge like the definition of the square root within 1/10, at other times by treating as done something that has not been done. The only progress resulting from the review of arithmetic is the following: I have said that, in the lower classes, the calculation of certain quotients or of certain roots led one to notice that a number might have infinitely many digits. This discovery now becomes, in a way, official. It becomes completely so when the sequence of digits is periodic, since one does study periodic decimals, and almost completely so for other sequences, since it is shown that the square root of an integer cannot be a fraction.

This is insignificant progress. In my opinion, the review of mathematics that is intended in the mathematics program of the last year is completely abortive because it does not clarify the central concept, namely, that of a number. One should not expect to find elsewhere what does not appear in the review of arithmetic. In algebra and geometry, the students are at the same time using the concept of an incommensurable number (which we assume already acquired by the pupils) and operations on these numbers (which are also assumed known).

15 *The use of Dedekind cuts.*   The gap is so shocking that in the colleges and universities we finally (!) give a definition of irrational numbers that is not required by the syllabus and which one is surprised to find out of its natural place. Most often Dedekind cuts are used. We deal a little with the arithmetic operations, though not enough to determine the digits in the results. Besides, we avoid speaking of the expression of irrational numbers in the decimal system of numeration.

Thus, for those who pursue their studies beyond the secondary level, the concept of a number is squarely faced. However, it is not done in the elementary form of a sequence of numbers in which it was first presented to everyone and in which we encounter it constantly. It is done only in an infinitely abstract form. A number is then a partition into two classes possessing certain properties, of all the rational numbers, that is, of all the pairs of these metaphysical entities that are called integers.

We can understand that such a presentation is not made in the mathematics program of the last year in high school. But even the students in the universities can themselves understand something of this presentation only when they give it a concrete meaning, when they represent points on a straight line following or preceding each other. And, with this translation, the definition of irrational numbers is just as understandable to final year high-school students. It consists in showing that to every cut there corresponds a definite segment. Now, this is established in the terminal high-school program not once but seven or eight times. Every time that one compares proportional magnitudes, passage from the commensurable to the incommensurable case is made by virtue of such a verification. Examples are the comparison of arcs of a circle with the central angles; areas of rectangles having the same base with the altitudes of these rectangles; volumes of right prisms of the same base with the altitudes of these prisms; and areas covered by a uniform motion with the duration of the motion. This same fact appears again when we wish to speak of the ratio of two quantities of the same kind, while respecting the doctrine, which I for one do not understand, according to which it is necessary to distinguish the ratio from the number that measures it. It is thus necessary to give definitions of two equal ratios or of one ratio that is greater than another. For example, we say that the ratio S_1/S_2 of two segments is equal to or greater than the ratio s_1/s_2 if, for any integer p, when we divide S_2 into p equal portions and also divide s_2 into p equal portions, S_1 always contains at least as many portions resulting from the division of S_2 as s_1 contains portions resulting from the division of s_2. And this definition is the comparison of two cuts. The same fact is again used to define π. In short, the exposition before which we retreat when it would be convenient for defining irrational numbers is actually made many times. Thus, it would be possible and even economical to give such an exposition.

However, that would not be sufficient. It would also be necessary to speak of operations on irrational numbers. Formerly, the possibility and even the meaning of these operations resulted from the "generality of analysis." In my youth, we "passed to the limit." I believe that nothing has changed for our high-school students, that everything is still a matter of using a few magic words when we are passing from operations on commensurable numbers to operations on arbitrary numbers. To change this, it would be necessary to adjoin to the definition in terms of cuts, an exposition that we tend to avoid, by stating, not without reason, that it would take too much time and exceed the level one can aspire to in the last year of high school.

16 *Advantages of the proposed exposition.* The exposition that I am proposing is not open to these objections or to any other if we dismiss once and for all those involving metaphysics and the use of a particular system of numeration. Being always essentially the same from the primary level to the threshold of advanced instruction, this exposition would be developed according to the age of the students. To the young we would primarily state the facts without proof, just as is done now. Some proofs would be given to older children. We might prove everything that can be proved if this is felt to be indispensable, although this is not my viewpoint. In any case, all proofs would appear clearly to everyone as a logical justification of facts already known, accepted, and used.

At the college level, students would have the maturity to follow a more complete analysis of the procedures previously used to define numbers. They would be shown what there is about this procedure that is too particular and unnecessarily precise. To determine and hence to be able to define, a number, it is not sufficient to locate it in terms of the loose scale of integers. We need to construct new numbers (forming what is known as an everywhere-dense set), the set of terminating decimal numbers in my exposition, a set chosen in too precise a manner. Utilizing a procedure that is constantly employed in mathematics, the classical exposition embeds this particular set in the larger set of commensurable numbers. Finally, when the comparison set is an infinitely tight mesh, the remaining numbers are defined by their places with respect to the numbers already defined. And this is the method of cuts.

In addition to these advantages, we must mention another, which is of considerable significance at the present time when lightening of the curriculum is such a pressing necessity: two chapters on arithmetic, the ones on fractions and decimals, can be omitted, and, as a consequence, there may be other items that can be deleted.

17 *Details of the proposal.*   I have emphasized several times that I was going directly from the integers to numbers in general. The time has now come to make precise just what I mean by that. I do not mean that I have any objections to speaking about the multiplication of decimals, for example, just a few minutes before speaking about the multiplication of numbers in general. Quite the contrary, I, too, see the advantages of being able to make concise, clear statements and to justify them with less difficulty. What I mean is that it is useless to make a separate, complete theory regarding decimal numbers. For example, if I needed to speak about multiplication to students and not teachers, after I made the general definition of multiplication that I used above, I would illustrate it first for the case in which the two numbers are both decimal numbers and only afterwards for the general case. In this way, I would have the rule for operating with terminating decimals a few minutes before the general rule. However, *I would not demonstrate the properties of multiplication until I got to the general case.*

Except with regard to details of the discussion, the terminating decimals and the commensurable numbers will only appear as particular cases. Thus, we should not need to speak a single word about the theory of fractions since the fraction a/b would simply be the exact quotient of a divided by b and the operations on fractions

$$a \div \frac{c}{b} = \frac{ab}{c}, \qquad \frac{a \cdot b}{b \cdot c} = \frac{a}{c}, \cdots$$

would only be particular cases of operations on numbers. Thus, we should not say a word about the theory of fractions in the last high-school grade because it would no longer be useful for the clarification of the concept of a number or of the rules on operations. Of course, we should no longer need to speak of the conversion of ordinary fractions into decimals or of repeating decimals.

But would we still speak of fractions at the primary level or in the first two grades of the secondary level? No, since this is not essential for the theory and serves no practical purpose. I believe that people will agree with me when I say that performing operations on twenty-seconds and thirty-sevenths is a martyrdom that we inflict on twelve-year-olds out of pure sadism without any justification based on usefulness as an extenuating circumstance. Yes, I know that by searching hard, one can find certain "applications" of fractions, that certain mechanics make calculations with fractions in cutting threads on screws. But not one in ten of them has established any relationship between the practice of his trade and the instruction received in school, and when, by exception, such a relationship is established, one may assert that the screw has explained the fractions rather than the other way around.

In the earlier grades, the reform that I am suggesting may seem to amount to replacing the word fraction with some other word, ratio, for example. For we do need to deal with the properties

$$\frac{a}{b} + \frac{c}{b} = \frac{a+c}{b}, \qquad \frac{ab}{bc} = \frac{a}{c}$$

and to give the corresponding rules for calculating the ratio of two numbers (*any* two numbers, not necessarily integers). However, the reform would be effective if we agreed to have the children no longer study two kinds of numbering, namely, numbering in terms of $n$ths for commensurable numbers and the decimal numbering system, that is, if we permitted them to answer 0.428 where the answer is 3/7.

True, *a* divided by *b* or *a/b* is still read "*a* bths" when *a* and *b* are integers, but this way of speaking no longer compels us to develop the entire theory of fractions any more than the word quatre-vingt-douze [French word for ninety-two, literally, "four twenty (plus) twelve"] compels us to study the numbering system with base twenty.

18 *Objections.* I can hear all the teachers protesting. Some of them are protesting because fractions provide innumerable exercises for their young pupils. After a moment's alarm, they will see that there will always be plenty of exercises. The complaint of the others moves me somewhat more, and, to tell the truth, I make the complaint myself: "To drop the theory of fractions from the mathematics program in the last year of high school is to cancel an admirable chapter. Of all those that we still have, it is perhaps the only one that is not there exclusively for its immediate use and that gives a feeling of pure beauty."

Let us recall what we say in our discussions with teachers of other fields: The lack of practical application of a subject does not make its teaching more disinterested but rather risks making it of no interest to the student. Because all specialties make a real contribution to our culture and since all of them exact long periods for learning the techniques, a person will, where possible, choose those fields whose techniques are of the greatest practical use. Certainly the teacher should take advantage of opportunities to make his students aware of the sheer beauties of a subject, but beauty is not teaching material and any pretensions to that effect will twist taste and form snobs. All this is valid for others and equally valid for ourselves. This is why we have seen, at different levels of our teaching, the disappearance from the curriculum of quite beautiful subjects that have had to yield to others that were more immediately useful for everybody. Let us take an example that is old enough for all controversy to have calmed down. It is not without regret that teachers have witnessed the disappearance of Diophantine analysis and the theory of continued fractions. Is it not natural, however, that these disciplines which are quite interesting from the mathematical point of view but highly specialized and without any practical importance, should be taught only to a small circle of chosen students?

In general, although the finite, exact calculations, the only ones that the ancients admitted, have retained their mathematical importance and although they need to be known and studied by present-day mathematicians, their practical importance has considerably diminished and at times has disappeared entirely. Everywhere, these "exact" calculations have been dethroned by approximative calculations, and, quite frequently, exact calculations are taken into consideration only because they lead to the simplest method of approximative calculation. In the universities, we no longer try to increase indefinitely the cases in which we can integrate a differential equation or evaluate an integral exactly, as was done formerly. We go as fast as possible over these techniques, which are no longer consistent with the other chapters where one studies integration without appeal to exact explicit expressions. Similarly, we no longer occupy ourselves with the algebraic solution of equations.

The concept of exact calculation varies from one of these questions to the other, but in both the word "exact" applies to a method of avoiding use of the infinite. But, the notion of the infinite is admitted in practice, where the concept of a limit is not mysterious since two sufficiently close states are practically identical. The mathematician, since he is obliged, in imitation of the Greeks, to avoid the use of limits, has had to develop methods—new arithmetics and new algebras—where the operations are defined only for those expressions that are treated as exact, or, more correctly, as existent. Pure and applied mathematics are divorced. The more elementary the level of teaching, the more the point of view of applied mathematics must be taken into consideration. However, it would be deplorable for the progress of mathematics if there were no instruction addressed only to mathematicians, in which the other point of view was adopted.

Suppose that we classed all exact expressions in order of complexity. Before those containing integrals, before those containing only the symbols of the elementary functions, even before those containing only algebraic radicals, we would find the expression a/b, which is the simplest of all exact expressions. It was the only truly exact expression for the Greeks because for them rational numbers were the only ones that could be attained or grasped, the only ones that were completely free of any notion of infinity.

It is clear that it is a survival of these out-of-date ideas that makes us cling so to rational numbers. We hold to them as the only remnants of a vanished teaching. Would it not be more worthwhile to recognize that the place for the study of rational numbers is no longer in the last year of high school and that there would be no disgrace in dropping the chapter on fractions in this class? The disgrace is to be found elsewhere. It is not something to fear for the future; it already exists. What is disgraceful is that in certain countries, in France, for example, it is possible to complete one's studies as a mathematician without ever hearing of these new arithmetics and algebras of which the study of fractions, treated as pairs of numbers, is only an introductory chapter and which form one of the most active branches of present-day mathematics.

19 *Distances and ratios of lengths.* The modification that I am suggesting consists therefore in replacing, in the arithmetic program, the chapters on fractions, decimal numbers, repeating decimal fractions, and approximative calculations with a single chapter on lengths and operations performed on numbers.

In a sense, this chapter would also be the first one in geometry, and there would then be a basis for speaking of the distance between two points in geometry. At the present time, we do not speak of numerical distance in the first book on geometry. We speak of it only in the third, having spoken of the measure of angles and arcs in the second. We still speak of it with some reticence because of the use of a number in its full generality. We speak about ratios of distances much more than we do about distances, and the distance numbers show up openly only when we cross-multiply the parts of a proportion involving distances. At that time,

both the distance numbers and the operations on numbers are assumed
known. What is the origin of this traditional order? We can only make
conjectures.

Although the act of measuring lengths is very ancient, it is certain
that the need of doing it with precision was felt only after astronomy came
to require precise measurement of angles. Graduated circles are perhaps
the earliest precision instruments. The teachers must have spoken to their
students of these wonderful instruments very early, and the actual measure
of angles and arcs may have therefore assumed a scientific character long
before this was true of lengths. Thus, it was natural and necessary to
treat the measure of arcs and angles in geometry. As for distance, it was
a fundamental concept. People spoke of it when they used it, that is,
in connection with the theorem of Thales. But it was precisely here that
the scandal of incommensurability appeared. It was necessary to go around
the difficulty, to avoid numbers. This is why people sometimes (as I
mentioned in § 15) give a definition of equality or inequality of two
ratios by means that are exactly those making it possible to decide the
equality or inequality of two numbers determined by cuts, but taking
pains not to notice this fact and to avoid speaking of these numbers that
they are comparing. They then pretend that they are not dealing with
numbers, that a ratio of lengths is a different thing from the number
that measures this ratio. Unless it is merely a question of observing that
4 may just as well be a number of rabbits as a ratio of two lengths, as I
have said, I do not understand either the significance of this distinction
nor the interest in it. Here, I can see only anxiety to avoid a word, and I
am reminded of a person who says, "I have no need for the concept of
a hat in order to talk about that round thing that you have on your head
with a leather band on the inside and a ribbon on the outside."

I have no fear of exhibiting my complete lack of comprehension of a
distinction to which certain people hold strongly and which appears
comical to me. For it is in comparing our mentalities frankly that we shall
discover the best ways of understanding each other and consequently of
teaching.

20 *Ratios and numbers.*   Although I do not see any advantages
in the method of exposition that I have just described, I must say that it
seems entirely satisfactory to me from a logical point of view, and the
theorem of Thales on the equality of two ratios that are not numbers is

rigorously proven. However, when we remove the denominators of a proportion among distances, we pass brutally to the equality of two ratios that are numbers. It would therefore be an enormous logical error if we did not at least establish a link between the ratios that are numbers and those that are not. This error is rarely committed in the crude form in which I have just imagined it, although examples could be cited. However, people often come close to it, and they do not come to the conclusion, which forces itself on me, that a ratio serving only as a number should be considered only in this form in teaching. Its other form, the one that I do not understand, is that of a metaphysical entity.

The error was never committed in former times when one deduced the equality $AB \cdot GH = CD \cdot EF$ of areas from the equality $AB/CD = EF/GH$ of segments. At least, one then would have been able to present the reasoning in a manner so as not to commit the error. But by the precept of Descartes, we have renounced the interpretation as an area of every product of numbers representing lengths. We should also apply it to the ratio of two numbers representing lengths. All these numbers, ratios, products, etc. are numbers—nothing more. But, of course, as I have said, when one speaks of 4, it is necessary to know if 4 is a number of rabbits, a ratio of lengths, a product of lengths, etc.

Finally, in our proposed curriculum, since we have defined a measure of AB in terms of the unit CD in a preliminary chapter, we no longer have any definition to give for the ratio AB/CD. This ratio has been defined; it is a number and is written in the decimal system.

21 *Proofs.* Here is how the proofs will be presented. The geometrical theorem of Thales will be proven in the ordinary manner: Parallel lines or planes that intercept equal segments of one transversal will also intercept equal segments of any other transversal.

This being the case, suppose that there are parallel elements intercepting segments AB and CD on one transversal and $A'B'$ and $C'D'$ on another transversal. We already know that if AB is one, two, three, ... times CD, then $A'B'$ will be one, two, three, ... times $C'D'$. More generally, let us compare the measure of AB in terms of the unit $U = CD$ with the measure of $A'B'$ in terms of the unit $U' = C'D'$.

From what was said above, we obtain the same lower approximating value in the first stages of the two measuring operations; that is, the integral parts of the two measuring numbers that we seek are the same.

In the second stage, we need to use the units U_1 and U_1' contained ten times in U and U' respectively. Now if U_1 is laid off ten times along AB and if we draw lines parallel to the given lines at the nine dividing points, they will divide $A'B'$ into ten segments that are equal to each other and hence to U_1'. Thus, parallel elements establish a correspondence between U_1 and U_1' just as between U and U', and, at the second stage in the measuring operation, we obtain the same lower approximating value. In other words, the first digit after the decimal point is the same for the two measuring numbers that we are seeking. Continuing this way, we arrive at $AB/CD = A'B'/C'D'$.

The proof seems to take the most natural form that anyone might wish: We have to prove that two numbers are equal. These two numbers have been defined digit by digit. By applying the definition, we show that they are identical digit by digit.

And the method of proof will be the same in all cases.

Is it a matter of the proportionality of central angles with the arcs that they intercept? Having explained the procedures for measuring angles and arcs[1] and having shown that equal central angles intercept equal arcs, to compare $\widehat{AOB}/\widehat{COD}$ with $\overset{\frown}{AB}/\overset{\frown}{CD}$, we take $\widehat{COD}$ as the angle unit and $\overset{\frown}{CD}$ as the arc unit and we measure $\widehat{AOB}$ and $\overset{\frown}{AB}$. The values obtained at the corresponding stages of the two measuring operations are the same; hence the conclusion.

---

[1] We will still be using the decimal system of numbering, even if it is with degrees, minutes, and seconds. We take the sexagesimal second as the principal unit; minutes and degrees are only groups of units.

With regard to angles and arcs, the binary system of numeration would be more suitable in one respect. Let me explain.

A measuring operation assumes that a unit U has been chosen. It postulates the existence of the auxiliary units U_1, U_2, ... (where $U = 10U_1$, $U_1 = 10U_2$, ...). It takes a more or less concrete form only when we know how to construct U_1, U_2, ... I have avoided these difficulties because, with final-year high-school students it is not important whether we admit an extra axiom or not. Therefore, we may admit the existence of the U_i and we may also dispense with their construction since it is a matter of operations that we imagine but do not actually perform.

In other cases, we would have had to prove the theorem of Thales in the form given in the text (parallel elements that intercept equal segments of one transversal intercept equal segments of any other transversal) and to deduce the construction of U_1 by starting with U (hence the existence of U_1). It is only then that we could have spoken of the measurement of lengths.

In the case of angles (or arcs), knowing U does not enable us to construct U_1. However, we know how to construct v_1, v_2, ... (where $U = 2v_1$, $v_1 = 2v_2$, ...). We might thus indicate the operations for comparing an angle with U, v_1, v_2, ... by means of a symbol in the binary system. Now, to every symbol in this system there corresponds a symbol in the decimal system and vice versa. U_1 is thus indicated by the binary symbol 0.000 1100 1100 1100 .... This proves its existence and gives a theoretical construction of it.

Finally, suppose that it is a matter of comparing two distances AB and CD covered by uniform motion in the time intervals from an instant τ_1 to τ_2 and from τ_3 to τ_4. Taking the length CD as the unit, we measure AB. With the interval (τ_3, τ_4) as a unit of time, we measure the interval (τ_1, τ_2). At every stage in the measuring operations, we have the same results and hence deduce the proportionality of the distances to the time intervals.

22 *Angles and arcs.*   In what follows, the reader will see that I constantly use analogous procedures. Right now, I should point out an apparent contrast between these procedures and those that have been followed in the second book on geometry for the past thirty years, since these latter tend to avoid the use of numbers as much as possible.

When I was a child, it was shown that equal central angles intercept equal arcs. We then passed to the measurement of angles and arcs and afterwards we proved statements such as the following: An inscribed angle is measured by one half the arc intercepted by its two sides. Now, the order of the theorems and their formulation are modified. Statements like the following are justified: An inscribed angle is equal to one half the central angle subtended by the arc intercepted by the sides of the given inscribed angle. One passes to the correspondence between equal central angles and equal arcs. Then, one arrives at the measurement of arcs and angles.

The source of this transformation is the remark, made I think by Hadamard, that there is no more need to bring measurement into the study of equality of angles or arcs in the second book than in the first book of geometry. This is a perfectly correct remark, designed to reduce theorems to their actual content and to prove them without appealing to anything that is not strictly necessary. It was proper to correct the awkwardness in language, as a result of which the concept of measure seemed to be involved in the statements and proofs when this was actually not the case. However, the change in the order was not necessary and many teachers have kept the former order.

This change in order is clearly bad when one writes, as I have seen, "Now that we have seen that the evaluation of inscribed, interior, and exterior angles of a circle can be derived from the evaluation of central angles, we shall proceed to study central angles." This transition, which is meant to be clever and pretends to be natural, goes against good sense.

Children understand the protractor in practice. It is the use of a protractor that is being justified in this chapter. It is shown that the protractor can be used for *measuring* central angles and then for *measuring* other angles. This explains the old form, which I repeat was awkward, of the theorems. Furthermore, it is highly probable that historically the ancient scientists found themselves in a position comparable to that of our students. The use of graduated circles must have preceded any theory, and it is the legitimation of this use that must have led to the theory of measure of the various angles. However that may be, we see that the new order is in no way responsible for the progress achieved, which consists only of modifications in the formulation of the theorems, since the proofs remain the same as before. We shall lose nothing of this progress since we shall not bring number in its full generality into the discussion except where this is indispensable (I have said this and shall not come back to it) in the comparison of arcs or angles with other arcs or angles.

The error that was committed consisted in introducing numbers conceived in all their generality where integers would have been sufficient. For example, to evaluate the ratio of a central angle to the corresponding inscribed angle, which is equal to 2, two general numbers were used: the measurements of the two angles in terms of a single arbitrary unit. Not only was one measuring operation replaced with two, which probably was more a bit of clumsiness than an error (simple failure to observe economy), but these measuring operations are completely different. The first is a finite operation requiring only one step and using only the concept of an integer. The other two are infinite operations requiring an infinite number of steps and necessitating the most general concept of a number.

23 *Scales and indirect comparison.* It would seem that the principle of economy would always require that we evaluate ratios directly and not as ratios of measurements. However, in practice, all lengths are measured in meters, all angles in degrees, etc.; that is, we employ auxiliary units and, as it seems, with only the disadvantage of having two measurements to make instead of one. Sometimes, this is because of experimental difficulties or impossibilities that prevent the direct comparison of lengths or angles. But there is also another reason.

In a geometrical problem, one needs to compare two lengths, for example, and only those two. It is quite different in practice when one encounters a hundred lengths and may expect to have to compare these lengths two at a time in all possible manners. Thus, it is a sensible and economical procedure to measure each new length. One single measurement for each length, made as precisely as possible, gives the ratio of the length in question to each other length. This explains the fact that in practice comparisons are never, or almost never, made directly but through comparisons with a standard scale.

It is the same in geometry. There, the precision must be indefinite, but to suppose that a length L has been measured is to suppose that one has compared it with an everywhere-dense set of lengths l such that the measurement determines exactly all the ratios L/l and hence the ratio of L to every other length. Thus, all comparison is made by means of an intermediary standard scale. For example, we have seen that one compares all collections of objects with a model collection, seemingly the least interesting of all of them since it is only a collection of conventional words, and that one compares distances with a scale that is infinitely subdivided into meters, decimeters, etc.

This procedure will be constantly encountered, and I shall not dwell any longer on this point.

III

AREAS

Just as before, I shall begin with an exposition. To avoid any misunderstanding, let me make clear that, in my opinion, this exposition would have to be shortened, for example, by omitting proofs of certain points, in order to be within the comprehension of the average student of the final high-school year. In no way do I put this forward as a plan to follow for this grade. Only experience can enable us to judge to what extent these suggestions may be adopted. I only make this exposition as a starting point for our discussions.

24 *First exposition and grids.* Suppose that we have a number of square tile blocks all of the same size and that we wished to cover the floors of several rooms with them. Suppose that, for *this* room, we need one hundred blocks placed properly and all used up by breaking some of them up if necessary and that, for *that* room, we need one hundred and fifty blocks. We say that the first room has a smaller area than the second and we make this statement more precise by saying that the first has an area equal to one hundred tile blocks and the second an area of one hundred and fifty tile blocks.

It is easy to see that this practical question and others like it have led to mathematical concepts, just as the comparison of a segment with a unit segment has led to the concepts of length and number.

To evaluate the lengths of the different segments AB laid off along a straight line, we made on that line (see section 8), beginning with a point ω and going in both directions, graduations in units U, in units U_1, etc. And it is this comparison of AB with the complete graduation T, with infinitely small intervals, that made it possible to define and evaluate the length of AB. We shall now proceed in exactly the same manner.

Suppose that we have a square C in a certain position in the plane under consideration and that ωx and ωy are straight lines containing two of its sides. Let us draw parallel to ωx all the lines whose distances from ωx are integral multiples of the side of the square C, and let us draw lines parallel to ωy in the same manner. We thus cover the plane with a grid R of squares equal to C, which we shall call U-squares. Let us divide the sides of these squares into ten equal parts and, at the points of division, let us draw lines parallel to ωx and ωy. We thus obtain a grid R_1 of squares, which we shall call U_1-squares. Similarly, we proceed to a grid R_2 of U_2-squares, etc. The collection of all these squares yields what we shall call the complete grid T derived from C. It is by a comparison with T that we shall define and evaluate areas.

Consider a domain D.[1] Let us count the number of U_i-squares that consist entirely of points in D. Let us say that there are n_i of them. Since a U_i-square contains one hundred U_{i+1}-squares, we have

$$n \le n_1/100 \le n_2/100^2 \le n_3/100^3 \cdots,$$

all these numbers are said to be at most equal to the area of D. Let us see how many U_i-squares there are with at least some points belonging to D. Let us say that there are N_i such squares. Obviously, $N_i \ge n_i$, and, for the same reason as above,

$$N \ge N_1/100 \ge N_2/100^2 \ge N_3/100^3 \cdots :$$

all these numbers, which are at least equal to the preceding ones, are said to be at least equal to the area of D.

When these two sequences approach each other arbitrarily closely, that is, when $(N_i - n_i)/100^i$ tends to zero as i increases without bound, we say that the number defined by these two sequences is the area of D in terms of the unit U.

As in the case of lengths, this definition provides an experimental procedure for determining the number defined. In either case, it is impossible to realize the complete graduation T, but we can at least mark the first few graduations R, R_1, R_2, for example, in the units U, U_1, U_2.

---

[1] In elementary geometry, the word "domain" does not have a precise meaning. It would become perfectly clear if we confined ourselves to the family of polygonal domains or the family of domains each bounded by a finite number of line segments and arcs of circles, etc. But to show that the definition is the same for all these families of domains, we have purposely allowed the word "domain" all its imprecise generality.

Use of this word would, from a strictly logical point of view, require that we prove those properties of these domains that we use, for example, the properties regarding boundaries. But here again, it is a matter of properties that are perfectly clear for certain simple families of domains and that we customarily and constantly admit without proof in elementary courses.

When it is a matter of lengths, these graduations are marked along a rule that is then placed along the segment to be measured and we read the sequence of numbers n, n_1, n_2; N, N_1, N_2. If it is a matter of area, we mark these grids on a transparent sheet of paper which is then placed on the domain being studied and we again read n, n_1, n_2; N, N_1, N_2.

25 *Rectangles.* We shall clarify this definition by applying it to a rectangle $OACB$ with sides OA and OB parallel respectively to ωx and ωy. Following the usual custom, we take the side v of U as unit of length, and we designate by a and b the lengths of OA and OB.

The sides of U_i parallel to ωy graduate OA into segments $v/10^i$. All the points of a_i of these segments belong to OA; at least some of the points of A_i of them belong to OA. The values $a_i/10^i$ and $A_i/10^i$ are approximating values of a from below and above respectively (see section 8). Also, $A_i \leq a_i + 2$.

If we reverse the roles of OA and OB and of ωx and ωy, we have similarly $b_i/10^i \leq b \leq B_i/10^i$.

Now, the n_i U_i-squares that have all their points belonging to $OACB$ are the ones whose projections onto OA and OB fall in the a_i segments contained in OA and the b_i segments contained in OB respectively. Thus, we have $n_i = a_i \times b_i$.

The N_i U_i-squares that have at least some points belonging to $OACB$ are those whose projections onto OA and OB are respectively the A_i and B_i segments referred to above. Thus, we have $N_i = A_i \times B_i$.

The product ab lies between the two numbers

$$\frac{n_i}{100^i} = \frac{a_i}{10^i} \times \frac{b_i}{10^i}$$

and

$$\frac{N_i}{100^i} = \frac{A_i}{10^i} \times \frac{B_i}{10^i}$$

provided by the U_i-squares. Thus,

$$\frac{N_i - n_i}{100^i} = \frac{A_iB_i - a_ib_i}{100^i} \leq \frac{(a_i + 2)(b_i + 2) - a_ib_i}{100^i}$$

$$= \frac{2}{10^i}\left[\frac{a_i}{10^i} + \frac{b_i}{10^i} + \frac{2}{10^i}\right] < \frac{2}{10^i}(a + b + 1).$$

Thus, the two sequences $N_i/100^i$ and $n_i/10^i$ approach each other arbitrarily closely. The value that they define is ab. In terms of the unit U, the rectangle $OACB$ has an area equal to ab.

Thus, it has been proven that every rectangle with sides parallel to ωx and ωy has an area, and we have evaluated that area. It follows from the expression obtained that the area is the same for two rectangles obtained from each other by translation and that the area of a rectangle with sides parallel to ωx and ωy formed by combining two other rectangles is equal to the sum of the areas of these other two rectangles.

For the mathematical concept of area to agree with the empirical idea and for it to be usable for any kind of polygon, we obviously need to show that every polygon has an area, we must evaluate that area, we must show that two polygons formed from each other by any movement have the same area, and that a polygon formed by the combination of two other polygons has an area equal to the sum of the areas of the original two polygons.

26 *Every polygon has an area.* Suppose that P is a polygon and that N_i and n_i are the numbers pertaining to this polygon that are provided by the U_i-squares. We need to evaluate $N_i - n_i$. Now, this number is the number of U_i-squares included in the N_i besides the n_i squares. That is, it is the number of U_i-squares that contain both points belonging to P and points not belonging to P. Such a square contains points of the boundary of P. This boundary is made up of a finite number of line segments. Thus, it will be shown that $(N_i - n_i)/100^i$ tends to zero as i increases without bound if we can show that $\mu_i/100^i$ tends to zero, where μ_i is the number of U_i-squares that contain points of an arbitrary segment AB. Now this is easy to establish.

Suppose first of all that AB is not parallel to either ωx or ωy. Let λ be a rectangle with sides parallel to ωx and ωy and suppose that the sides of λ that are parallel to ωy intercept on the line AB a segment $\alpha\beta$ containing the segment AB. The U_i-squares that contain points of AB are among the squares that contain the points belonging to λ. If there are N_i squares of the latter type, the number $\mu_i/100^i$ is at most equal to $N_i/100^i$; that is, it is at most equal to the value approximating the area of λ from above. For sufficiently large i, this approximating value exceeds this area by an arbitrarily small amount. If a and b are the sides of λ, then, for sufficiently large i, the ratio $\mu_i/100^i$ will exceed ab by as small an amount as we wish.

Suppose that γ is the midpoint of $\alpha\beta$. We start over with our reasoning for $\alpha\gamma$ on one hand and $\gamma\beta$ on the other. We replace the figures λ, $\alpha\beta$ by similar figures λ_1, $\alpha\gamma$; λ_2, $\gamma\beta$. λ_1 and λ_2 have dimensions $a/2$ and $b/2$. For a U_i-square to contain points of $\alpha\beta$, it must contain either points of $\alpha\gamma$ or points of $\gamma\beta$, and therefore, for sufficiently large i, the ratio $\mu_i/100^i$ exceeds the quantity

$$\frac{a}{2} \cdot \frac{b}{2} + \frac{a}{2} \cdot \frac{b}{2} = \frac{ab}{2}$$

by as small an amount as we wish.

Similarly, a new subdivision would yield $ab/2^2$, then $ab/2^3$, etc. Thus, $\mu_i/100^i$ can be as small as we wish for sufficiently large i.

If AB is parallel to ωx or ωy, we replace λ with a rectangle whose base is AB and whose altitude is arbitrarily small.

27 *Sum of polygons.*   If we divide a polygon P into polygons $P_1, P_2, \ldots P_m$, we have

area of P = area of P_1 + area of P_2 + $\cdots$ + area of P_m.

Indeed, the n_i U_i-squares contained in P are either contained entirely in one of the polygons P_k (say n_k^i squares in P_k) or they contain points on the boundaries of P_k. Let μ_i be the number of these squares. Thus we have

$$n_i = n_1^i + n_2^i + \cdots + n_m^i + \mu_i.$$

Now, if i increases without bound, the ratio $n_i/100^i$ and the ratios $n_k^i/100^i$ approach arbitrarily closely to the area of P and the areas of the P_k, since $\mu_i/100^i$ tends to zero. From this, we have the stated equality.

As a consequence, area of P > area of P_1 + $\cdots$ + area of P_m for the case of a polygon P containing polygons $P_1, P_2, \ldots P_m$ without common interior points and not covering all of P, and area of P < area of P_1 + $\cdots$ + area of P_m for the case of a polygon P formed by the union of polygons P_k that have common interior points.

28 *Conditions for existence of an area.*   In a classroom, it would be advisable to complete the treatment of the polygonal case before considering other domains. Addressing the teachers now, I shall avoid the otherwise inevitable repetitions by speaking of the necessary and sufficient condition for a domain D to have an area.

We have seen that it is necessary for the number $(N_i - n_i)/100^i$ to tend to zero as i increases without bound. The ratio $N_i - 100^i$ is the area of the polygon E formed by the N_i U_i-squares that are used. The polygon E covers D. The ratio $n_i/100^i$ is the sum of the areas of the polygons I formed by the n_i U_i-squares that are used. I is covered by D.

Therefore, for a domain D to have an area, it is necessary that it can be covered by a polygon E and that it in turn cover polygons I without common interiors in such a way that the area of E exceeds the sum of the areas of the I by an arbitrarily small amount. The converse is also true since, for sufficiently large i, the N_i' U_i-squares containing points of such a polygon E have an area exceeding the area of E by an arbitrarily small amount and the total area of the I exceeds the area of the n_i' squares consisting only of points of I by an arbitrarily small amount. Since (with N_i and n_i the usual numbers with respect to D)

$$N_i' \geq N_i \geq n_i \geq n_i',$$

the ratio $(N_i - n_i)/100^i$, which is less than $(N_i' - n_i')/100$, which in turn exceeds the difference area of E − area of I by as small an amount as we wish, is also as small as we wish. Furthermore, the area of D lies between the areas of E and I.

The application of this statement to the extension of the statements of the preceding section—and also to the proof that the area of a domain resulting from the union of several other domains has an area if these other domains have areas—is immediate. It will also enable us to give a more general significance to the following section.

29 *Congruent domains.*   Two equal polygons have the same area. More generally, if D is a domain with an area and if Δ is congruent to D, then Δ has an area, and this area is equal to the area of D. We shall divide the proof into several parts, supposing first that D is a polygon and making hypotheses concerning the nature of the motion that takes D into Δ.

(a) *The polygon Δ is obtained from D by a translation.* D is covered by N_i U_i-squares of which it contains n_i. The translation transforms the U_i-squares into V_i-squares of the same area (see section 25). Therefore, Δ is covered by N_i V_i-squares and contains n_i V_i-squares, so that

$$\frac{n_i}{100^i} \leq \text{area of } \Delta \leq \frac{N_i}{100^i}.$$

This shows that Δ and D have the same area.

(b) *The polygon* Δ *is obtained from D by a reflection about the axis* ZZ'. Suppose that C' is a square one side of which lies along ZZ'. Starting with C', let us construct a grid T' in the same way as we constructed the grid T starting with C in section 24. The successive squares of T' are designated by U', U'_1, U'_2, ... Suppose that N'_i is the number of U'_i-squares containing points of Δ and that n'_i is the number of U'_i-squares containing only points of D. All the U'_i-squares have the same area (see section 29a). There are 100^i of them in C'. Their area (see section 27) is equal to $S/100^i$, where S is the area of C'. Therefore,

$$\frac{n'_i}{100^i} S \leq \text{area of } D \leq \frac{N'_i}{100^i} S,$$

and, as i increases without bound, the difference between the two outside members tends to zero since (see section 26) $(N'_i - n'_i)/100^i$ tends to zero.

Because of the symmetry of T', D, and Δ with respect to ZZ', the numbers N'_i and n'_i are valid also for Δ and hence the area of Δ also verifies the preceding inequality. Therefore, Δ and D have the same area.

(c) *The polygon* Δ *is congruent to the polygon D.* Suppose that A, α and B, β are two pairs of corresponding points belonging respectively to D and Δ. The translation $A\alpha$ transforms B into β'. Then reflection about the perpendicular bisector of $\beta\beta'$ transforms D into D' in such a way that A is at α and B is at β. Thus, either D' coincides with Δ or D' is a reflection of Δ in the line $\alpha\beta$. In both cases, we pass from D to Δ by a succession of transformations that leave the area invariant. Hence, D and Δ have the same area.

(d) *D is a domain possessing an area.* Suppose that E and I are two polygons, the first covering D and the other covered by it, and that their areas differ by less than ϵ. The displacement that transforms D into Δ transforms E and I into polygons of the same area and one of these polygons covers Δ and the other is covered by Δ. Since the difference ϵ between these areas is arbitrarily small, Δ has an area. This area differs from that of E by less than ϵ. Therefore, D and Δ have the same area.

The result that we have just obtained can also be formulated as follows: The area of a domain does not depend on the position of the given unit square C but only on its dimensions; that is, since we agreed to take the side of C as our unit of length, the area depends only on the unit of length.

Suppose that C and C' are two squares and that T and T' are two corresponding grids that can be obtained from them. To evaluate the area of a domain D starting with C', it is necessary, for example, to count the numbers N_i and n_i relative to D and T'. These numbers are also the ones that apply to Δ and T, where Δ is what D becomes as a result of the displacement that transforms C' into C. Thus, if D has an area with respect to C', then Δ has an area with respect to C, and the two areas are equal. Now, since Δ and D are congruent, D also has an area with respect to C and it is equal to the area of Δ with respect to C. Therefore, D has an area both with respect to C and with respect to C' and these two areas are equal.

The preceding two statements can be summarized in a single statement: a relative displacement of a domain and a grid T has no influence either on the existence of the area of the domain or on the value of this area.

30 *Change of unit length.* Let us now examine the effect of a change in the unit of length, that is, the replacement of the square C with a square C' of different size, on the existence of the area of a domain D and on its value. In other words, let us look at the question analogous to the one that led us to multiplication in section 11.

Let us suppose that in the case of C the numbers of squares U_i are N_i and n_i and that the boundary of D can therefore be covered with polygons (namely squares U_i) whose total area in terms of the new unit of length is $(N_i - n_i)S/100^i$, where S is the new area of C. Now, by hypothesis, $(N_i - n_i)/100^i$ tends to zero as i increases without bound since we assume that D has an area with respect to C. Therefore, D also has an area with respect to C'. Since this area A' lies between $N_i(S/100^i)$ and $n_i(S/100^i)$, no matter what the value of i is, it is equal to the area A of D with respect to C multiplied by S. Thus, $A' = AS$. If c is the new length of the side of C, we write $A' = A \cdot c^2$.

The change in unit of length has the effect of multiplying all the areas by the square of the length of the original unit of length with respect to the new one.

This proposition, which expresses the effect on the comparison of D to C of a similarity transformation of one of the two domains D and C, may like the preceding proposition be stated in a converse form.

Let us keep C fixed and let us replace D with a similar domain D', where the ratio of similitude is k. If C' denotes the transform of C in the similarity transformation of ratio k, the numbers N_i and n_i relative to C

and D on the one hand and C' and D' on the other are the same. Thus, D' has an area with respect to C', and this area is equal to the area of D with respect to C, say A. Therefore, the area of D' with respect to C exists and is equal to Ak^2, since k^2 is the area of C' because k is the length of a side of C'.

Thus, a similarity transformation of ratio k transforms a domain D with area A into a domain D' with area Ak^2.

31 *Axiomatic definition of area.*   The properties of areas that we have just proven are completely in accord with the methods of using area in practice, and in fact it is because of this agreement that we may feel that we have adequately translated into mathematics the common notion. However, if there were other ways of assigning numbers to domains that also possess the properties that we have derived above for those numbers that we have been calling areas, then there would be several possible mathematical translations of the concept of area, and we might fear that we have not chosen the best. Therefore, even when we consider mathematics as an experimental science, it is important to show that the *areas that we have just considered are completely determined by the following conditions:*

α—*To each domain in a family of domains to which all polygons belong there corresponds a positive number which we call its area.*

β—*The area assigned to a domain formed by the union of two disjoint domains is the sum of the two areas.*

γ—*To two congruent domains correspond equal areas.*

Furthermore, it can be seen that

δ—*The area numbers are completely determined numerically when we know the area assigned to one of the domains.*

Let us take any square C and let k^2 be the number associated with C. Then, if D is any domain of the family and if N_i and n_i are the numbers relative to D and to the grid T constructed from C, then the area of D is between $N_i(k^2/100^i)$ and $n_i(k^2/100^i)$, so that it is the one that our procedure enables us to assign to D when we take for the square of area 1 the transform of C with the ratio $1/k$. Furthermore, the number k is known: If σ_0 is the known area of the domain D_0 and if σ is the area that our procedure allows us to assign to D_0 with the aid of the grid T (that is, if σ is the limit of the numbers $N_i/100^i$ and $n_i/100^i$), we have $k^2 = \sigma_0/\sigma$.[1]

Properties α, β, and γ constitute the axiomatic definition of area, freed of the too particular features that use of the grid T seemed to have for defining area. The grid T plays in the concept of area a role analogous to that of the decimal system of numeration in the conception of the general idea of a number.

32 *Decomposition of polygons.* We use primarily the following property, which follows from α, β, and γ: Two polygons that can be decomposed into congruent polygons, that is, two polygons that result from two different arrangements of the same polygonal parts have the same area.

We have proved this property even for the case of two domains that result from two different arrangements of parts of arbitrary form, provided each of these parts has an area, and we can therefore now go back to the classical exposition. Thus we can legitimately find the area of a parallelogram in the ordinary manner, then that of a triangle, and from them the area of any polygon since every polygon can be decomposed into triangles. The results can be summarized in the classic theorem: *Suppose that ABCD . . . is a plane polygon π and that O is a point in its plane. Then the area of the polygon is equal to*

$$\tfrac{1}{2}[\pm\ AB \times \text{dist } O,\ AB \pm BC \times \text{dist } O,\ BC \pm \ldots].$$

The sign in front of the term PQ will be $+$ *or* $-$, *depending on whether O is on the same or opposite side of the segment PQ as the part of the polygon π adjoining PQ.*

To justify this statement, we point out (it is assumed that the area of a triangle is known) that the sides of the triangles OAB, OBC, . . . , which we shall call the triangles T_i, partition the plane into partial poly-

---

[1] In fact, this proof assumes that D belongs simultaneously to the family of domains for which our procedure in the preceding paragraphs is applicable and to the family of those domains to which the theorem of this paragraph assumes that a number satisfying conditions α, β, and γ is assigned. However, it is a matter of proving that conditions α, β, and γ are sufficient to define areas of the domains D that were considered above. Therefore, we should confine ourselves to the family of these domains or to a more restricted family.

If, on the contrary, we took a larger family, the conditions α, β, and γ could still be satisfied. However, as I proved elsewhere, we would no longer have proposition δ. In other words, properties α, β, and γ would not be sufficient to characterize area up to a change in the unit of area.

of the polygon onto the axis $O\Omega$. The number assigned to the polygon is completely independent of the choice of O. We shall soon see that it is positive.

First, we show that this number verifies property β. To do this, we take the sum of the numbers assigned to two disjoint polygons P_1 and P_2 whose union forms a polygon P. These two numbers are evaluated with the aid of a single point O. The number assigned to a polygon $ABC\ldots$ is not changed by inserting a vertex Z on the segment AB between A and B, that is, by replacing $AB \times$ dist. (O, AB) with $AZ \times$ dist. $(O, AZ) +$ $ZB \times$ dist. (O, ZB). We may therefore assume that P_1 and P_2 are adjacent everywhere along certain sides. Then, if AB is one of these sides, $AB \times$ dist. (O, AB) shows up in the numbers assigned to P_1 and P_2, but with different signs since P_1 and P_2 are on opposite sides of AB.

On the other hand, if KL is a side of P_1, for example, that does not belong to P_2, the product $KL \times$ dist. (O, KL) shows up in the numbers assigned to P and P_1, this time with the same sign since P and P_1 are on the same side of KL.

Therefore, after cancellation of similar terms in the sum of these expressions for the numbers assigned to P_1 and P_2 with the aid of O, we find the expression for the number assigned to P with the aid of O.

Now that property β is proven, the number assigned to the polygon will be the sum of the two numbers assigned to the triangles of any one of the decompositions of P into triangles. Therefore, this number will be positive and will satisfy condition γ if the number assigned to a triangle is positive and independent of the position of the triangle in the plane.

Now, let us calculate the number relative to a triangle ABC, taking O at A. We find it equal to $\frac{1}{2}BC \times$ the altitude passing through A.

The proof is now complete. It is usually given in the following form: O is fixed. Proposition β is proven. Having reduced the calculation of the number assigned to P to the addition of the numbers assigned to triangles just as above, one then shows directly that the three products obtained by multiplying the sides of a triangle by the corresponding altitudes are equal and that whatever the position of the point O may be with respect to a triangle, the number assigned to the triangle is equal to half that product. These are the assertions that we have replaced by the more compact but less elementary reasoning concerning the passage from O to O'. Thus, the proof reduces to this: From hypotheses α, β, and γ, there arise innumerable ways of calculating area. We choose one that is well defined. In this way, we satisfy the principal part of condition α: To every domain, we assign a definite number. Then, we show that this number satisfies conditions β and γ and that it is positive.

34 *Critique of the two expositions.* This is exactly what we did in our first exposition except that we did not specify which properties of actual area we utilized in our mathematical construction. Thus, we did not state principles α, β, and γ. In fact, the order that we followed is precisely the one that is always followed when one needs to translate a concrete notion into mathematics. We begin by using *everything* that experience has taught us about the idea. Then, when we have succeeded in drawing up an initial mathematical definition, we can set about clarifying it by determining precisely what has been used properly. The axiomatization is made last—after the essentials have already been treated. Then, however, it fixes precisely the significance of the results obtained, lays the basis for generalizations, etc.

Thus, except for the details of exposition, our two methods follow the same path. Hence, one cannot accuse the second method of being a mere verification without reproaching the first for the same thing.[1] One cannot reproach the first for the artificial use of the grid T without reproaching the second for its use of the point O. The only profound difference is the fact that the first, by using a general definition of area, can be applied to a greater number of cases, whereas the second, by using a method of evaluation that applies especially to polygonal areas, is of more restricted application. It offers, however, the elegance of finite processes, and it sets apart polygonal domains in the manner in which rational numbers are ordinarily distinguished from other numbers, as mentioned in the preceding chapter.

35 *Third exposition. The method of surveyors.* By using these remarks, we could now draw up new expositions of the theory of areas. Here is the only one that is worth noting at this point. In the second procedure, we applied in effect the formula for integration in polar coordinates and in the first we applied the formula for integration in rectangular coordinates. Obviously, we could particularize and, by following

---

[1] A characteristic common to all proofs of the existence of a quantity E. Assuming tentatively the existence of E, one makes a construction of E and verifies that this construction satisfies all the required conditions.

surveying procedures, we could obtain a finite method that is applicable only to polygons. One would proceed as follows.

α—When a direction ωy has been chosen, we assign to every polygon P the number $\frac{1}{2}(B_1 + b_1)h_1 + \frac{1}{2}(B_2 + b_2)h_2 + \cdots$, where B_1, b_1; B_2, b_2; ... are the lengths of the bases of the trapezoids into which P is decomposed by the lines parallel to ωy drawn through the vertices of P and h_1, h_2, ... are the corresponding altitudes of these trapezoids.

Here, a triangle with one side parallel to ωy is treated as a trapezoid. For such a trapezoid, one of the two bases is of zero length.

β—Consider a trapezoid (or triangle) T with bases parallel to ωy. Let us partition it into T_1 and T_2 by a secant that touches its bases (not their continuations). It follows from the construction that the number (T) assigned to T is the sum of the numbers (T_1) and (T_2) assigned to T_1 and T_2. This is a particular case of proposition β.

Another particular case is that in which T is divided into T_1 and T_2 by a line parallel to the bases. Thanks to the preceding case, we may assume that T is a triangle ABC with base BC parallel to ωy. We let DE be the secant. The number (T) is $\frac{1}{2}BC \cdot$ dist. (A, BC) or, as is immediately verified, $\frac{1}{2}AB \cdot$ dist. (C, AB). Now,

$$\begin{aligned}
\tfrac{1}{2}AB \cdot \text{dist.}\,(C, AB) &= \tfrac{1}{2}AD \cdot \text{dist.}\,(C, AD) + \tfrac{1}{2}DB \cdot \text{dist.}\,(C, DB) \\
&= \tfrac{1}{2}AC \cdot \text{dist.}\,(D, AC) + \tfrac{1}{2}BC \cdot \text{dist.}\,(D, BC) \\
&= [\tfrac{1}{2}AE \cdot \text{dist.}\,(D, AE) + \tfrac{1}{2}EC \cdot \text{dist.}\,(D, EC)] + \tfrac{1}{2}BC \cdot \text{dist.}\,(D, BC) \\
&= \tfrac{1}{2}AE \cdot \text{dist.}\,(D, AE) + [\tfrac{1}{2}DE \cdot \text{dist.}\,(C, DE) + \tfrac{1}{2}BC \cdot \text{dist.}\,(D, BC)] \\
&= (T_1) + (T_2).
\end{aligned}$$

Consider now the general case of a polygon P partitioned into two adjoining polygons P_1 and P_2. To evaluate the numbers (P), (P_1), and (P_2) assigned to these polygons, we can use the decompositions made by all the lines parallel to ωy passing through the vertices of the three polygons, whereas the definition uses only certain ones of these parallels because of the second particular case that we studied.

Let us examine the contributions to (P), (P_1), and (P_2) made by trapezoids bounded by two consecutive lines parallel to ωy. The trapezoids that show up in (P) are partitioned (in the manner examined in the first particular case) by the sides of P_1 and P_2 (which are interior to them) into partial trapezoids of which some show up in (P_1) and the others in (P_2). Therefore, from the first particular case, $(P) = (P_1) + (P_2)$.

γ—To prove proposition (γ) it will be sufficient to evaluate the number assigned to a triangle ABC. We already know this number if one of the sides is parallel to ωy. Suppose that this is not the case and that it is the line drawn through C parallel to ωy that divides it into two triangles ACD and BCD. We then have

$$(ABC) = \tfrac{1}{2}CD \cdot \text{dist.} (A, CD) + \tfrac{1}{2}CD \cdot \text{dist.} (B, CD)$$
$$= \tfrac{1}{2}AD \cdot \text{dist.} (C, AD) + \tfrac{1}{2}BD \cdot \text{dist.} (C, BD) = \tfrac{1}{2}AB \cdot \text{dist.} (C, AB).$$

36 *Choice of expositions.* In teaching, should we adopt one of the three expositions that we have just obtained—all complete from a logical point of view—or should we take some other analogous procedure?

As I have already said, the first is probably too learned and complicated for average students and experience alone could decide this point. They should find the other two more accessible. However, it would be hard for students to understand the importance of this proof of α, β, and γ, which comes after they have already used the results many times. It might lead them to think that one may always call to question what has been proven, and give a peculiar idea of logical reasoning. In any case, it is certain that the second exposition is well known, that it has appeared for many years in textbooks, and that it nonetheless has not been used in teaching. Thus, teachers see no objection to admitting α, β, and γ, either implicitly or explicitly, and I agree with them. The important thing is to say nothing that is not strictly true about the exposition adopted. To this end the teacher must be well informed by a careful comparison of what is being done with what should be done if one wished to prove everything. Failure to do this has led some teachers into curious errors.

For example, it was believed that the classical procedures for transforming any rectangle R into a rectangle ρ, one side of which is of unit length, were sufficient to solve the area problem for rectangles, since the area of R would then be the length of the other side of the rectangle ρ. This is indeed one way of defining area; but it is not at all obvious that procedures other than the classical ones would not lead to a rectangle ρ also associated with the same rectangle R, but with a different area.

37 *Fourth exposition. Equivalence under finite decomposition.* Let us make this more precise by considering the case of equivalence under finite decomposition. Two polygons are said to be finitely equivalent if one can decompose each of them into the same finite number of pairwise congruent triangles. Let us show that every triangle is finitely equivalent to a rectangle ρ, from which it will follow that any polygon is finitely equivalent to a rectangle formed from a finite number of such rectangles ρ corresponding to the triangles into which the polygon can be decomposed.

Consider a triangle ABC. Suppose that A' and B' are the midpoints of CA and CB. Let us rotate the triangle $A'B'C$ 180° about the point B' into the triangle $B''B'B$. We transform ABC into a parallelogram $ABB''A'$. Let M be any point on $A'B''$. If we subject the triangle $AA'M$ to the translation AB, we get the parallelogram $ABNM$. We proceed in the same manner with it. Thus, since we can reverse the roles of A and B, we can transform $ABB''A'$ into any one of the parallelograms of the same base AB and of the same corresponding altitude.

These parallelograms $ABDE$ include those for which AE is an integral multiple of a given length l.

For example, if $AE = 3l$, by partitioning AE into three equal parts and drawing parallels to AB through the points of division, we partition $ABDE$ into three equal parallelograms which, when rearranged, will form a parallelogram $\alpha\beta\delta\epsilon$, where $\alpha\beta$ is three times AB and $\alpha\epsilon$ is equal to l. If we now proceed with $\alpha\beta\delta\epsilon$ as we did with $ABB''A'$, letting $\alpha\epsilon$ play the role of AB, we can get any of the parallelograms of base $\alpha\epsilon$ whose parallel base lies along $\beta\delta$; in particular, we can get the one that is a rectangle.

If we take $l = 1$, we transform the triangle ABC into a rectangle ρ one of whose sides is equal to 1. What is the other side?

The base of $ABB''A'$ is AB and its corresponding altitude is one half the altitude of ABC that passes through C. In the shift from $ABB''A'$ to $ABMN$, AB remains the same, as does the corresponding altitude, but the other base and the other altitude do change. However, if we note that the product of a base and the corresponding altitude is the same for both bases of a parallelogram, we see that the product remains in the change from $ABB''A'$ to $ABMN$ and in all the subsequent transformations. It follows from this that if b is the base of ABC and h is the corresponding altitude, the product of the base and the altitude is $\frac{1}{2}bh$ for all the parallelograms obtained.

The second side of the rectangle ρ is therefore $\frac{1}{2}bh$. More generally, for any given polygon P, we have learned, by decomposing P into triangles and by transforming each triangle into a rectangle ρ, to transform P by means of finite equivalence into a rectangle of which one side is 1 and the other side is equal to the sum $\Sigma \frac{1}{2}bh$ taken over the different triangles in question.

Does this give us a complete theory of areas? No, since it is not proven that the area obtained is unique, that is, independent of the areas of the triangles resulting from the decomposition. To believe otherwise would be making the very mistake we so often criticise in our students when they jump to the conclusion that there is only one way in which a number can be decomposed into prime factors because they have shown that a particular procedure of decomposition yields a definite result.

Explicitly, we have seen that two polygons cannot be transformed into each other by finite equivalence *with the aid of our procedure* except when the numbers that we have assigned them are the same. But we also know that this condition is sufficient in the case of two parallelograms. From this it immediately follows that it is sufficient for any two polygons. From this result, one may show that *if it is possible to satisfy α, β, and γ*, the area numbers are determined up to a factor, which proves δ.

Thus, this fourth theory on areas is exactly equivalent to the classical theory.[1] Like the latter, it rests on α, β, and γ, proves δ, and provides a determination of areas as far as polygons are concerned.

To complete this fourth theory, we must prove α, β, and γ (for example, by one of the three procedures we have indicated). Since we are dealing only with polygons, the last two are especially indicated. The simple form that one can then give to the second method can be seen in Hilbert's *Grundlagen der Geometrie*. The third can be used in a similar way. If simplifications are possible it is because now, even more clearly than before, everything reduces to showing that the number defined is well determined. For if this is the case, β and γ automatically follow since, in the case of β, the number is defined by a decomposition of the polygon and, in the case of γ, it is defined for a triangle independently of its position.

38 *The role of numbers.* Thus, the theory is complete when we prove that it is impossible to partition a polygon into a finite number of polygonal pieces in such a way that the pieces arranged in a different way will form a polygon lying entirely within the original one. This property is the geometrical foundation for the theory of areas. For polygons, this theory can be divided into three parts:

---

[1] Though more elegant than the classical theory, this fourth theory has the drawback that it cannot be carried over to volumes. Dehn has shown that two polyhedra with the same volume cannot in general be transformed one into another by finite equivalence.

1° Every polygon is equivalent under finite decomposition to a rectangle, one side of which is equal to a given segment.

2° Two such rectangles are not equivalent if their other sides are unequal.

3° Measure of the second sides.

The third part has to do with the measurement of lengths, the introduction in fact of the general concept of a number. The other two assume the concept of an integer only, and for that reason we say that they are of a purely geometrical nature. However, whereas we have proven the first part by a purely geometrical reasoning, the proof indicated for the second part appeals to the third part and hence to the concept of a number in general.

Up to the present time, no one has been able to prove the second part, that is, the geometric fact that is at the base of the theory of areas of polygons, by the method of equivalence under finite decomposition, without appealing to the general concept of number. In fact, it is the concept of area, acquired elsewhere one might say, that justifies in retrospect the method of equivalences.

39 *The possibility of a geometric proof.*   However, this geometrical fact is so familiar to us from our everyday experience that it is hard to realize that it needs to be proven. Isn't it actually just a matter of the space occupied by a region independently of its position in space and of the arrangement of its parts? This *space* is the area, and the number of which we had been speaking is simply the measure of the area—a measure which should not be confused with the area itself.

Here, in spite of the banality of the word "space," we recognize a metaphysical presentation resembling the presentation of the integers that I criticized. An integer is the common property of all the collections derived from a single collection by changing the order and nature of the objects composing it. An area is what is common to all the domains derived from a single domain by the change of position and arrangement of the parts belonging to it. A metaphysical integer had a decimal notation. A metaphysical area should then have a measure; this would be a metaphysical number that could be expressed in the decimal system.

And when one thinks of what a metaphysical nonintegral number is, one can see to what extent these entities are superimposed. But since all this is mathematically useless, this metaphysical presentation of the definition is never presented frankly. For many, however, the area has remained different from the number that measures it. As for myself, the use of the word "measure" in the expression "measure of areas" has the same meaning as for the expression "measure of lengths." This usage reminds us that we must have chosen a unit in order to be able to speak of area or length, these latter quantities being numbers. It is only these numbers that are used in mathematics. Everyone is free to add metaphysical notions to these mathematical ones, but the former should neither intrude in teaching nor be used to judge the logical value of a theory. The error concerning the area of rectangles, of which I have spoken, no doubt stems from the following fact: Even while examining whether the existence of area had been proven logically, there still lingered the idea that area is a fundamental concept the existence of which does not need to be proven.

There was a time when the fact that we are discussing resulted from a very handy axiom: *The whole is greater than the part.* This axiom was used for length, area, and volumes. How have we managed to dispense with it?

For length: the axioms dealing with motion, which we have used, imply in particular that if AB is displaced along the line containing it in such a way that A is moved to a position between the original positions of A and B, then B will be moved outside the original positions. This is the axiom, "The whole is greater than the part," which we have therefore admitted again in a more precise form.

For areas: The three methods that we have mentioned derive the result that the two rectangles $1,h$ and $1,h'$ are not equivalent from the fact that the lengths h and h' are not equivalent. The axiom for areas was derived from the axiom for lengths. We again encountered nonintegral numbers in our proofs because we were reasoning in terms of the sides of different rectangles and one always uses numbers to individualize and distinguish the different segments. It is true that this use can be disguised. However, if this were done, it would still not be the purely geometrical proof, which, as I have said, no one has yet constructed. And, from what has been said, it does not seem likely that anyone will ever be able to do so since, to be really different from the above proof, such a purely geometrical proof must not use the axiom with regard to lengths.

40 *Pedagogical conclusions.*   Now that we know the exact content of the classical theory, the obstacles to completing it, and the pedagogical objections to the use of a logically complete exposition, we are in a better position to make certain improvements in teaching.

I shall suggest only two. One of them is incidental, namely to dispense with the theorem that the areas of two rectangles with a common side are proportional to the length of the other sides and to obtain directly the area of a rectangle as in section 25, that is, as is done at the primary level and again in the study of integral calculus. It would be faster and more natural and would avoid useless lengthy discussions if we would admit that a ratio of areas is a ratio of numbers. The method that would be employed would be one that the more intelligent students would actually be able to reinvent themselves. And we would not be tempted to invoke a grandiloquent theorem regarding magnitudes that are proportional to other magnitudes—a theorem that some may possibly understand but which neither the students nor I understand at all. I shall deal later on with this theorem in discussing the measure of magnitudes in general.

The other improvement would be of greater importance. It would consist in admitting that area is not a fundamental concept and in giving it the definition appearing in section 24. This definition could be lightened since we would not use it as a starting point for our reasoning. We would state only that this theorem makes it possible to prove the propositions of sections 26–29, *which would be stated without proof.* Then we should resume the classical approach. This procedure is already more or less what is followed by certain teachers. It is the procedure of Claude Guichard's textbook on geometry.

41 *Areas bounded by circular arcs.*   To bring out the significance of this modification, let us first discuss thoroughly the question of areas of domains bounded by arcs of circles and segments of straight lines.

The area of a circle. Let p_K be a regular polygon of K sides inscribed in a circle C and let P_K be a regular polygon of K sides circumscribed about C. The numbers n_i and N_i relative to the circle lie between the numbers n_i' relative to p_K and N_i'' relative to P_K irrespective of the values of K and i. Now, as i increases without bound, the ratios $n_i'/100^i$ and $N_i''/100^i$ tend to the areas of p_K and P_K. The first of them increases and the second decreases. Therefore, the fractions $n_i/100^i$ and $N_i/100^i$ lie between the area p_K and the area of P_K. Now, by section 30,

$$\frac{\text{area of } P_K}{\text{area of } p_K} = \left(\frac{\text{radius of } C}{\text{apothem of } p_K}\right)^2 = \frac{R^2}{a_K^2},$$

so that

$$\text{area of } P_K - \text{area of } p_K = \text{area of } p_K \times (R^2/a_K^2 - 1),$$

which obviously tends to zero when $1/K$ tends to zero. Thus, a circle has an area, which is equal to the limit of the areas of p_K and P_K.

At the same time, we have shown that the area of the U_i-squares necessary to cover an arc of a circle tends to zero as i increases, and hence that any domain bounded by line segments or arcs of a circle has an area.

Area of a sector. For an example, suppose that $\alpha = 4235.43 \ldots$ is the central angle of a sector, measured in sexagesimal seconds. If S is the area of the circle, since this circle contains $360 \times 60 \times 60$ sectors each with a central angle of 1 second, each of them has an area s equal to $S/(360 \times 60 \times 60)$ and the sector in question has an area between $4235\ s$ and $4236\ s$. The area of a sector of central angle 0.1 second is $s \times 0.1$ since there are 10 of these sectors in one sector of area s. Therefore, a sector of central angle α has an area between $4235.4 \times s$ and $4235.5 \times s$, etc.

Here, the reader will recognize the mode of reasoning which I have several times recommended and which is the reasoning used at the primary level. I shall not refer again to the needless precision of the use of the decimal system of numeration in this reasoning.

When the area of a sector is obtained and the properties α, β, γ, and δ are established for regions bounded by straight lines and arcs of circles, the theory of areas of these domains is complete.[1]

42 *Hypocrisy and errors.* Now let us compare this exposition with that found in the textbooks. To be sure, they differ only slightly, but they differ on an essential point, namely, the textbooks give an *arbitrary* definition for the area of a circle. Natural, yes, but arbitrary from a logical point of view.

For some twenty-five years, all the textbooks have, in effect, adopted a

---

[1] Naturally, the area S of a circle ought to be calculated. According to section 30, it is of the form πR^2, but the relationship between the number π and the length of the circumference cannot be established until we have dealt with the lengths of curves.

procedure that consists in saying that the limit of the areas of the p_K will, by definition, be called the area of the circle. Some textbooks then prove the existence of such a limit, and others assume it, but this is of slight importance.

Formerly, during my childhood, for example, it was stated simply that since the polygons p_K differ by less and less amounts from the circle, the area of the circle is the limit of the areas of the p_K. The texts dealt with area (considered a fundamental concept) both of circles and of polygons, and relied on properties that were not stated but assumed. Obviously, this was not satisfactory from a logical point of view, although nothing incorrect was said. In contrast, the present exposition, in my opinion, is marred by a gross error, not against logic but against common sense, which is more serious. At the same time, there is manifest a naïve faith in the power of words according to which one can overcome a difficulty by a verbal artifice—as if real progress could be achieved so cheaply!

What actually is it that is done? The area of the circle is the limit of the p_K. This is an arbitrary definition, a label that could be replaced by any other. It follows that adopting this definition instead of another is not sufficient to ensure that the number called the area of the circle will discreetly hasten back to the family in which the properties α, β, γ, and δ are true. Therefore, we cannot logically derive the area of a sector from a known area of a circle; to believe it and to make a supposed proof is to err gravely. The area of the sector is, *by definition*,

$$S \frac{\alpha}{360 \times 60 \times 60}.$$

From the area of a sector, so given by definition, one cannot derive the area of a segment by a process of reasoning. It is by definition that the area of the segment is the difference between the area of a sector and the area of a triangle.

If the limit of the p_K had been designated the "tarababump" of the circle, one would certainly not be permitted to derive from it the value of the tarababump of the sector and the segment. We allow ourselves to do this because instead of the word tarababump we used the word area! Here is a gross offense to common sense. There are ways of pretending that one is not guilty of it, but the reader should imagine the inevitable confusion that will be caused by making the pupils identify this new area with the areas to which they are accustomed. We are free to choose between error and hypocrisy.

Furthermore, one should not feel that one can escape by repeating three times the magic words "by definition" for the circle, the sector, and the segment because areas so defined cannot serve any purpose. It would be impossible to deal with any question, any problem on the subject of areas without running into propositions α, β, γ, and δ, which one would not have the right to use. For example, the classical question of the lunes of Hippocrates could not be solved.

Therefore, one must have the concept of area before calculating areas—a concept implying properties α, β, γ, and δ for all the regions that one will be dealing with. The method of my childhood, which used these properties without explicitly stating them in the same manner for all regions, was better than the method used in present-day textbooks, which make an unfortunate discrimination between the different regions. The old method could have been made quite acceptable by avoiding the use of the idea of a limit region by saying that the area of the circle was between the areas of the inscribed polygons p_K and the areas of the circumscribed polygons P_K. This would agree essentially with the approach that I advocate here. Of course, in such a procedure, one must show or assume the existence of the area of a domain bounded by line segments or arcs after proving or assuming the existence of area for polygons.

Clearly, one may confine oneself to saying that the definitions of areas of a circle, a sector, and a segment are given in the chosen manner since it is with these definitions and with them alone that we have the propositions α, β, γ, and δ. However, this would mean admitting that it is not a question of arbitrary definitions, but that these definitions have been chosen instead of others as a result of investigations. One would not describe these investigations since the discussion of section 24 is enough for one to guess their nature.

43 *More general regions.* I have finished with the question of plane areas. However, to show the flexibility of the procedure advocated, let us consider the case of plane regions bounded by line segments and arcs of conics—regions that one sometimes encounters in elementary geometry. If such regions are bounded, do they have areas? In other words, can a finite arc of a conic be covered with polygons the sum of whose areas is arbitrarily small?

In the case of an arc of an ellipse, let us use the theorem on orthogonal projections. Suppose that D is a region and d is an orthogonal projection of D. In the plane of D, let us take the grid T whose sides are parallel to the intersection XX' of the planes of D and d, the angle between which is θ. The projection of a square U_i is a rectangle u_i. The side of u_i parallel to XX' is $1/10^i$; the side perpendicular to XX' is $\cos\theta/10^i$; the area of u_i is $\cos\theta/100^i$. Now, D contains n_i squares U_i and is contained in N_i of these squares. Thus, d is contained in the polygon formed by N_i rectangles u_i. The area of this polygon is $N_i\cos\theta/100^i$. It contains a polygon of area $n_i\cos\theta/100^i$. Therefore, if D has an area, then d has an area and the area of d = the area of $D \times \cos\theta$.

In the case of an arc of a hyperbola or parabola, one can similarly use a relation

$$\text{area of } d \leq \text{area of } D \times K$$

between the areas of the two polygons d and D, which are central projections of each other. In this relation, K is fixed for all pairs (d, D) situated in two bounded regions corresponding to each other by central projections. However, it is simpler and more general to prove that *every convex bounded arc can be covered by polygons, the sum of whose areas is arbitrarily small.*

Suppose that we have such an arc. Let us partition it into subarcs none of which touches any line parallel to either of the rectangular coordinate axes OX and OY at more than one point. The possibility of such a partition is immediate. However, it would be difficult to prove it in a precise manner, not because of the word "convex," but because the words "curve" and "arc" are not precisely defined in elementary geometry. We will, nevertheless, develop our reasoning from such a subarc. The proof will be valid for arcs formed by a finite number of these subarcs.

Suppose that Γ is such an arc entirely covered by the rectangle $AA'BB'$ with sides parallel to OX and OY, and suppose that two opposite vertices A and B are the ends of Γ. Let S be the area of this rectangle. Because of its convexity, Γ lies either entirely in the triangle $AA'B$ or entirely in the triangle ABB'. Let us suppose that it lies entirely in $AA'B$. It is possible to cover $AA'B$ with rectangles whose sides are parallel to OX and OY such that the sum of their areas exceeds the area of $AA'B$ by an arbitrarily small amount. Therefore, we may assume that this sum of areas is less than $\frac{2}{3}S$. Of these rectangles, we keep only those that contain points belonging to Γ and we reduce each of them to a rectangle with parallel sides just large enough to contain the same points of Γ. After making these modifications, we have rectangles whose total area is less than $\frac{2}{3}S$ and which contain respectively the arcs Γ_1, Γ_2, . . . whose union is Γ. If we repeat this reasoning for Γ_1, Γ_2, . . . , we cover Γ with rectangles whose total area is less than $(\frac{2}{3})^2 S$, etc. This completes the proof.

Thus, the elementary theory of areas that we have developed is applicable in particular to all bounded regions whose boundaries consist of a finite number of line segments or arcs of convex curves.

The above reasoning could prepare for, and possibly clarify, the arguments we will employ when dealing with the definite integral. Would not students understand more easily that in passing from elementary geometry to analysis nothing has been changed but the language, which was more geometrical beforehand but more analytic afterwards? And perhaps they would sense the progress made to some extent. In mathematics, the starting point is always concrete; the language is also concrete, and most often it is geometrical. This is helpful to the imagination, too helpful in fact, since reality is very rich and too many observations attract attention. The first steps in reasoning cannot get off the ground, burdened as they are by many of these special observations. Little by little, one isolates each question from the others and discerns what there is essential about each of them. The reasoning becomes more general while the language becomes more analytic and abstract. This abstract quality is not devoid of content; quite the contrary, the language has become abstract in order to be more immediately applicable to a greater number of real situations.

IV

VOLUMES

The chapter on areas was written in such a way that one might derive from it, paragraph by paragraph, a theory of volumes by making modifications that are almost always obvious and that frequently amount simply to substitution of words. In this way, one can obtain expositions concerning volumes corresponding to what I have called the first, second, and third expositions of the theory of areas. There can be no question of extending to volumes the fourth exposition, the one dealing with equivalence under finite decomposition, since Dehn has shown that two polyhedra of the same volume cannot always be transformed from one to the other by finite decompositions.*

I shall not develop these three expositions for volumes, but simply indicate the less obvious points that need to be modified in the preceding chapter. Furthermore, I shall not translate the first exposition paragraph by paragraph, *as it would be possible for me to do.* I shall shorten it by using the results obtained for areas.

44 *First method. Grid of cubes.* By means of a grid T of cubes, we can define volume just as area was defined in section 24. Then the word-for-word translation of section 25 will be replaced by what follows.

Let ωxyz be an orthogonal trihedral formed by three edges of a cube of the grid T. Let us consider a right prism or cylinder whose altitude is parallel to ωz. Suppose that the area of the cross section of the cylinder is B and the length of the altitude is H.

The planes of the faces of the cubes of T that are parallel to ωxy cut off on the altitude a complete graduation T_z made up of segments U_z of length one, of segments $U_{1,z}$ of length $1/10$, of segments $U_{2,z}$ of length

---

* Lebesgue evidently refers to M. W. Dehn's paper in the Göttingen Nachrichten for 1900. (Ed.)

$1/10^2$, etc. The planes of the faces of the cubes of T that are parallel to ωz form on the cross section of the cylinder a complete grid T_{xy} made up of squares U_{xy} of side 1, of $U_{1,xy}$ of side $1/10$, etc. This graduation and this grid make it possible to measure the length of the altitude and the area of the cross section. Suppose that $n_{i,z}$, $N_{i,z}$, $n_{i,xy}$, $N_{i,xy}$ are the measure numbers provided respectively by the segments $U_{i,z}$ and the squares $U_{i,xy}$. We know that $(N_{i,xy} - n_{i,xy})/100^i$ and $(N_{i,z} - n_{i,z})/10^i$ tend to zero as i increases without bound and that $n_{i,xy}/100^i$ and $n_{i,z}/10^i$ tend to B and H.

Since n_i and N_i are the numbers provided by the cubes U_i of T for the cylinder under consideration, we have $n_i = n_{i,z} \times n_{i,xy}$; $N_i = N_{i,z} \times N_{i,xy}$. Hence

$$\frac{N_i - n_i}{1000^i} = \frac{N_{i,z}}{10^i} \times \frac{N_{i,xy}}{100^i} - \frac{n_{i,z}}{10^i} \times \frac{n_{i,xy}}{100^i}$$

$$= \frac{N_{i,z} - n_{i,z}}{10^i} \times \frac{N_{i,xy}}{100^i} + \frac{n_{i,z}}{10^i} \times \frac{N_{i,xy} - n_{i,xy}}{100^i},$$

an expression that tends to zero. Therefore, the cylinder has a volume. The approximating values of this volume are

$$\frac{n_{i,z}}{10^i} \times \frac{n_{i,xy}}{100^i} \quad \text{and} \quad \frac{N_{i,z}}{10^i} \times \frac{N_{i,xy}}{100^i}.$$

Since the number BH lies between these two values, the volume is BH.

45 *Volumes of congruent figures.* This volume must therefore remain the same after a relative displacement of T and the cylinder such that ωz remains parallel to its original position or, of course, after a displacement that leaves the direction of ωx or ωy fixed.

We generalize this result by showing that if a body C has a volume, this volume remains the same after a relative displacement of C and T such that ωz remains parallel to its original position. Let C' be the new position of C with respect to T and suppose that Γ_i' and Λ_i (the figures formed respectively by n_i cubes U_i of T contained in C and the N_i cubes U_i covering C) are displaced along with C into new positions Γ_i' and Λ_i'.

Every cube U_i of Γ_i or Λ_i has been transformed by this displacement into a cube U_i' of the same volume. Therefore, if j is sufficiently large, the cubes U_j contained in U_i' have volumes whose sum is arbitrarily close to (but less than) $1/1000^i$, and the sum of the volumes of those that cover U_i' is also arbitrarily close to (but greater than) the same number. It follows that, for j sufficiently large, the cubes U_j provide for C' a value

$n'_j/1000^j$ greater than any specified number that is less than $n_i/1000^i$ and a value $N'_j/1000^j$ that is less than any specified number exceeding $N_i/1000^i$. Thus, for sufficiently large j, we have

$$\frac{N'_j - n'_j}{1000^j} \leq \frac{N_i - n_i}{1000^i} + \epsilon,$$

no matter how small ϵ is. In other words, C' has a volume and this volume, being the common limit of $n'_j/1000^j$ and $n_i/1000^i$, is also the volume of C.

Now suppose that C and C' are two congruent bodies and suppose that C has a volume. Let us denote by $\omega\zeta$ and $\omega\zeta_1$ the axes carried along by C into $\omega'\zeta'$ and $\omega'\zeta'_1$ when C coincides with C'. We suppose that $\omega\zeta$ coincides with ωz and that $\omega'\zeta'_1$ is parallel to and has the same positive direction as ωz.

Let us first rotate C about ωz in such a way that $\omega\zeta_1$ is brought onto the plane $\omega x z$. We then rotate C about ωy so as to bring $\omega\zeta_1$ into coincidence with ωz. We finally make a displacement that leaves ωz parallel to its previous position, but that brings $\omega\zeta_1$ into coincidence with $\omega'\zeta'_1$. C is thus brought into coincidence with C' by three volume-conserving displacements. Therefore, C' has a volume and it is equal to the volume of C.

46 *What figures have volumes.*   This result is property γ for volumes. Since properties β and γ and the effect of changing the unit are studied for volumes just as for areas, the theory of volumes is complete in a sense, except that we still do not know to what bodies this theory is applicable or whether all polyhedra, for example, are included in them.

Every polyhedron has a volume and, more generally, so does every region in space that is bounded by plane regions and portions of the lateral surfaces of cylinders whose cross sections have area. Indeed, we have seen that a cylinder whose cross section has an area has a volume if its generators are parallel to ωz, and hence (by section 45) regardless of its position. In other words, the total surface of such a cylinder can be enclosed in cubes U_i the sum of whose volumes is arbitrarily small for sufficiently large i. The same holds true *a fortiori* for a plane region cut from the base and for a part cut from the lateral surface. The theorem follows.

47 *A variant of the first method.*   Thus, it only remains to calculate the volume of different polyhedra. Before doing so, let us indicate
a variant of the first method, one that is applicable to the study of areas.

In that study, let us suppose that we had gone through sections
24–28. In place of section 29, we should reason as follows.

We have seen that the area of a rectangle with sides parallel to ωx
and ωy is the product of these sides. Just as before, it follows that a translation does not change areas. Let us examine the effect of a rotation on
a square of side c. We draw lines parallel to ωx and ωy, partitioning the
square in its new position into four congruent right triangles and a small
square. Suppose that a and b are the sides of the triangles with $a < b$.
The side of the little square is $b - a$. By translating two of the triangles,
we obtain, in addition to the small square of area $(b - a)^2$, two rectangles
each of area ab. Thus, we have a polygon whose area is (see section 27)

$$(b - a)^2 + 2ab = a^2 + b^2 = c^2.$$

Thus, the area of a square is independent of its position. Therefore,
for a region s possessing an area and having the numbers n_i and N_i,
after a displacement, the ratios $n_i/100^i$ and $N_i/100^i$ also represent areas
of two polygons, one contained in s and the other containing s. Thus, a
displacement has no influence either on the existence of an area or its
value.

Let us return to volumes. Suppose that, by following step by step
the exposition regarding areas, we arrive at the analogue of section 29.
We then say:

The volume of a cube is not changed by any sort of displacement.
Since such a displacement results from displacements in which one of
the planes ωxy, ωyz, or ωzx slides along itself, we may assume that ωxy
slides along itself. Suppose that $n_{i,xy}$, $N_{i,xy}$, $n_{i,z}$, $N_{i,z}$ are the numbers
relative to this cube (see section 44) before the displacement. After the
displacement, the numbers $n_{i,z}$ and $N_{i,z}$ remain the same, and the other
two become $n'_{i,xy}$ and $N'_{i,xy}$. Therefore, after the displacement, the volume
of the cube will be between

$$\frac{n_{i,z}}{10^i} \times \frac{n'_{i,xy}}{100^i} \quad \text{and} \quad \frac{N_{i,z}}{10^i} \times \frac{N'_{i,xy}}{100^i}.$$

The second factor in each of these products tends, as we saw in the study of areas, to the area of the base of the cube, which is independent of the displacement.

Now that the invariance of the volume of a cube is established, it follows that a displacement has no effect on the existence or value of volumes.

48 *Simplifications.*   Thus, there are several ways of presenting the first method, all rather long when they are explained completely. One could think up many others. All require, in addition, the calculation of volumes, which can be done by classical procedures. Here I should like to point out four simplifications. The first consists in calculating immediately the volume of a right prism (see section 44).

When this is done, we deduce in the ordinary manner that the volume of a prism with parallel bases is the product of the cross section by the length of an element. Then, instead of going through the gamut of the various parallelepipeds, we note that the two theorems on the projections of segments and areas yield

$$\frac{\text{area of cross section}}{\text{area of base}} = \frac{\text{altitude}}{\text{length of element}},$$

from which we derive that the volume is the product of the base and the altitude. This simplification is employed by many teachers. Apparently, the same is not true of the next simplification which rests on the discussion of section 44.

A region C that possesses a volume is transformed into a region C' of the same volume by a reflection, rectangular or oblique, through a plane P. Since we can take the grid T in any position whatever with respect to C, let us put faces of the cubes U in P. Symmetry transforms the cubes U_i into parallelepipeds Π_i whose bases parallel to P are equal to those of the cubes U_i and whose corresponding altitudes are also equal to those of the cubes U_i. Thus, parallelepipeds Π_i have the same volume as the cubes U_i. Now if n_i and N_i are the numbers pertaining to C, it follows that C' contains parallelepipeds Π_i having a total volume of $n_i/1000^i$, and is contained in parallelepipeds Π_i of volume $N_i/1000^i$. This proves the auxiliary theorem.

Returning to the classical method, let $ABCD$ be any tetrahedron. Consider the triangular prism $ABCDEF$ bounded by the planes ABC, DAB, DAC, plane $CBEF$ passing through CB parallel to DA, and plane DEF parallel to ABC. This prism is formed by three tetrahedrons $ABCD$,

EBCD, and *EFCD*. Any two of these tetrahedrons can be obtained one from the other by oblique reflection. For example, those that have a common face are symmetric about that face. Therefore, they have the same volume, which is one third the product of the base *ABC* and the altitude passing through *D*.

49 *Frustum of a pyramid.* The calculation of the volumes of polyhedra is virtually completed.[1] My fourth remark, quite incidental, has to do with the volume of the frustum of a pyramid. Let us generalize the figure that we have just been using by taking two triangles *abc* and *def* with parallel sides in the same sense. Consider the solid *S* bounded by these triangles and the planes *abde*, *bcef*, and *cafd*. If *def* is equal to *abc*, we have a prism. If *def* or *abc* is reduced to a point, we have a tetrahedron. In these three cases, the volumes are respectively HB, $HB/3$, and $Hb/3$, where B is the base in the plane *abc*, b is the base in the plane *def*, and H is the altitude. The first of these volumes can equally well be written Hb, $H(B/5 + 4b/5)$, or in many other ways. To get several expressions for the other two, we need to introduce another area than that of the base of the tetrahedron. Suppose that b_m is the cross section of the solid made by the plane equidistant from *abc* and *def*. For the prism we have $b_m = B = b$. For the tetrahedron, we have either $4b_m = B$ and $b = 0$ or $4b_m = b$ and $B = 0$. The three volumes can then be represented by the same formula: $H(\lambda B + \mu b + \nu b_m)$, where, in the case of the prism, $\lambda + \mu + \nu = 1$, in the case of the tetrahedron with $b = 0$, $\lambda + \nu \times \frac{1}{4} = \frac{1}{3}$, in the case of the tetrahedron with $B = 0$, $\mu + \nu \times \frac{1}{4} = \frac{1}{3}$, and hence $\lambda = \mu = \frac{1}{6}$, $\nu = \frac{2}{3}$.

This gives the formula

$$\frac{H}{6}(B + b + 4b_m).$$

The advantage to having common formulas in which B, b, and b_m appear linearly is obvious: The application of this formula can be extended to bodies that can be constructed from bodies for which it is valid (and relative to the same base planes) by combining several of these bodies, taking away others, etc.,—in short, by constructing a sort of algebraic sum of bodies.

---

[1] However, it would be good to prove this by showing that any polyhedron (convex or otherwise) is formed by the union of a finite number of tetrahedra.

The formula can be applied to a tetrahedron $BCDE$ with two vertices in abc and two in def since such a tetrahedron can be attained by removing from the prism $ABCDEF$ the two tetrahedrons $ABCD$ and $EFCD$.

The formula can be also applied to every solid S since S is made up of these three tetrahedrons $abcd$, $ebcd$, and $efcd$.

In particular, this can be applied to the frustum of a triangular pyramid and hence to the frustum of any pyramid, since such a frustum is formed by the union of frustums of triangular pyramids. Thus, if we denote by D, d, and δ the distances from the planes of B, b, and b_m to the apex of the pyramid, we have

$$\frac{D}{\sqrt{B}} = \frac{\delta}{\sqrt{b_m}} = \frac{d}{\sqrt{b}} = \frac{D - \delta}{\sqrt{B} - \sqrt{b_m}} = \frac{\delta - d}{\sqrt{b_m} - \sqrt{b}}$$

and, since the last two numerators are equal,

$$\sqrt{B} - \sqrt{b_m} = \sqrt{b_m} - \sqrt{b}, \qquad \sqrt{b_m} = \tfrac{1}{2}(\sqrt{B} + \sqrt{b}),$$

$$bm = \tfrac{1}{4}(B + b + 2\sqrt{Bb}),$$

and the volume is

$$H(B + b + \sqrt{Bb}).$$

This method of obtaining the volume of the frustum of a pyramid is both less natural and less rapid than the method that consists in taking the difference between two pyramids, but it brings out the importance of the formula involving the three levels, a formula to which I shall return.

50 *First exposition. Projections.* I have nothing further to say concerning the application of the first method to polyhedra. Therefore, I pass on to the second and third methods, consisting, let us recall, in employing first the classical arguments for evaluating volumes satisfying conditions α, β, and γ (assuming that it is possible to satisfy them), in using that very fact to prove property δ, and finally in showing that the numbers obtained do in fact verify α, β, and γ. By α, β, γ, and δ, I mean, of course, the statements of the theory of areas modified by replacing the words "area" and "region" by "volume" and "body."

The proof was constructed for areas by using formulas that, for polygons, follow from the quadrature formula in polar coordinates for the second method, and from the quadrature formula in rectangular coordinates for the third. For volumes we will use the application to polyhedra of cubature formulas in spherical, cylindrical, or rectangular coordinates, so that we have three procedures. The first of them is classical. I only point out the modification in presentation that is analogous to the one that I used in section 33, since it employs a theorem on the projection of areas that is not commonly used in classes despite its convenience.

We know that we orient a plane by taking an angle ωxy in that plane. What we call the angle between two oriented planes is the angle between the secondary axes ωy and $\omega y'$ of the two right angles that orient the plane S and that are drawn in such a way that their primary axes coincide on the line of intersection of the two planes. It is clear, that, depending on whether the cosine of this angle is positive or negative, the orientation given to one of these planes is or is not the same as the orientation of the same plane that results from the projection of the angle that orients the other. The absolute value of this cosine is the number that appears in the theorem on the projection of a given area in section 43.

But let us now give signs to areas. In a plane oriented by ΩXY, consider a domain to which we give the same orientations as an angle ωxy. Depending on whether the orientations of ΩXY and ωxy are the same or not, we assign the area of Δ (we are concerned only with domains that have areas) the sign $+$ or the sign $-$. Thus, when we project Δ orthogonally onto a plane oriented by the projection of ωxy, we have the formula for projections:

area of projection of Δ = area of $\Delta \times \cos$ (angle of projection).

Consider a polyhedron Π. Let ωxyz be a rectangular trihedral, which we move in such a way that ω never leaves Π. If we move ω in a face and turn ωz so that it is normal to that face and directed inward, then ωxy defines the orientation of the face. The theorem on projections is stated thus:

The sum of the areas of the orthogonal projections of the oriented faces of a polyhedron is zero.

Suppose that $F + F' + \cdots + F^{(k)}$ is that sum. If we draw the projections of the edges of the polyhedron, each projection of a face will be decomposed into polygons p. If we assign the areas P of these polygons the same signs as the projections of the faces from which they are derived, the sum can be written

$$(P_1 + P_2 + \cdots + P_k) + (P'_1 + P'_2 + \cdots + P'_k) + \cdots.$$

The same polygon p may appear several times in this sum at times as a positive and at times as a negative term. The theorem states that p gives as many positive as negative terms. To see this, let us drop a perpendicular from a point Ω in the interior of p to the plane of the projection H. Let us place on this perpendicular the axis ΩZ of a trihedral ΩXYZ with the same orientation as ωxyz. The face ΩXY determines the orientation of H. Let us also place ωxyz in such a way that ω coincides with one of the points of the boundary of Π that is projected onto Ω and so that ωz is normal to this boundary and is directed inward. Finally, let us rotate ΩXYZ around ΩZ and ωxyz around ωz so as to make ΩX and ωx parallel and with the same sense. Then, the cosine of the angle between H and the plane of the face oriented by ωxy is positive or negative (that is, p appears in the projection of this face in the form of a positive or negative contribution) according to whether the angle between ΩY and ωy is acute or obtuse, that is (since this angle is also the angle between ΩZ and ωz and since ωz is directed inward) depending on whether one enters or leaves the polyhedron at the point of projection Ω in question when moving along ΩZ in the positive direction.

But it is clear that in moving along the axis ΩZ for its entire length, one must pass as many points of entry as points of exit. This proves the theorem.

Application to the question in which we are interested is immediate. Let O be any point. Just as in section 33, one can show that the polyhedron Π is the algebraic sum of the pyramids with apex at O whose bases are the various faces of Π. By application of the formula found for the volume of a pyramid, we assign to Π the sum

$$\Sigma \tfrac{1}{3}\Phi_i \times \overline{H_iO},$$

where Φ_i is the area (positive) of a face φ_i, where H_i is the foot of the perpendicular drawn from O to φ_i, and where $\overline{H_iO}$ is measured in the same sense as ωz when ωxyz is put in the position that determines the orientation of φ_i.

It remains to show that this number is positive and that it satisfies conditions β and γ. This results immediately (see section 33) from the fact that it does not depend on O. Suppose that O is replaced by O'. The variation of the sum will be

$$\frac{OO'}{3} \Sigma \Phi_i \cos (\overline{OO'}, \overline{HO}) = \frac{OO'}{3} \Sigma \Phi_i \cos (\varphi_i, OXY),$$

where the trihedral $OXYO'$ is chosen so as to be trirectangular and possess the same orientation as ωxyz. According to our theorem on projections, the sum on the right side of this equation is zero, which proves the invariance of the number assigned to Π.

51 *Second and third expositions.* The other two procedures require the use of expressions for the volume of an arbitrary polyhedron that are derived from cubature formulas in cylindrical or rectangular coordinates. These two formulas include an integration with respect to z and a double integration with respect to x and y. These two integrations can be carried out in whichever order one prefers. This leads either to the decomposition of the polyhedron into frustums of prisms by drawing planes parallel to oz through the edges, or to a decomposition into slices by drawing planes parallel to oxy through the vertices.

Let us take the first decomposition. We need to evaluate the volume of each frustum of a prism by a double integral over the cross section of the prism. This integral is found with the aid of polar coordinates if we have been using cylindrical coordinates, and with the aid of ordinary Cartesian coordinates if we have been using Cartesian (three-dimensional) coordinates. These procedures yield the decompositions of the cross sections described in sections 33 and 35, respectively. They lead us to consider a polyhedron, in the first place, as an algebraic sum of frustums of triangular prisms with generators parallel to oz having in all cases an edge lying along oz and, in the second place, as a sum of frustums of prisms with generators parallel to oz and with cross sections that are trapezoids (that could reduce to triangles) with bases parallel to oy.

The only purpose in all this analysis was to get the necessary decompositions. Of course, in elementary expositions, one does not speak of integrals or of the origin of the decompositions that are given without preliminary explanation. One says: Let us decompose every polyhedron in such and such a manner into an algebraic sum of triangular or trapezoidal frustums and let us take the algebraic sum of their volumes, arbitrarily assumed given by the formula of the three levels. This sum is the number that we shall assign the polyhedron.

Of course, it would be necessary to verify α, β, and γ. I omit these verifications which one can easily imagine in each of the two cases that we have just considered and shall examine what decomposition into slices yields.

Calculation of the volume of one of these slices by means of polar coordinates is not elementary, since it involves subdividing the slice with hyperbolic paraboloids. However, ordinary rectangular coordinates give an elementary expression for it. To each lateral face of the slice we assign the frustum of a prism, with trapezoidal or triangular base, formed by segments of the lines projecting the points of the face on *yoz*, each segment having its endpoints on the face and *yoz*. The polyhedron is an algebraic sum of these prism frustums, so that we have again an expression for the volume of an arbitrary polyhedron which, as we can verify, satisfies α, β, and γ.

52 *The conditions α, β, γ by slices.*   We have just outlined three expositions, doing for volumes what is done in section 35 for areas. We now put the last of them in a form that is closer to that of section 35.

We decompose the given polyhedron into slices by passing planes through the vertices parallel to *oxy*. Each of these slices is a solid bounded by two polygons located in two planes parallel to *oxy* (which we shall call the base planes) and by trapezoids (or possibly triangles) whose bases lie in the two base planes. This decomposition shows that a slice is an algebraic sum of frustums of prisms with generators parallel to *ox* and with one base serving as a lateral face, trapezoidal or triangular, of the slice. The decomposition of each of the trapezoidal frustums by a diagonal plane makes it possible to consider only triangular frustums. Each of them, like a triangular prism, is decomposed into three tetrahedra. Finally, we may consider a slice as an algebraic sum of tetrahedra whose four vertices are in two base planes. Conversely, every algebraic sum of such tetrahedrons has the form of those bodies that we have been calling slices. Thus, the slices are polyhedra of the most general type, for which the considerations of section 49 legitimate the formula of the three levels. Consequently, to show that conditions α, β, and γ are compatible, we may argue as follows, guided by the preceding analysis but without making allusion to it.

Let us divide every polyhedron into slices by planes drawn parallel to *oxy*. Each slice has an altitude H_i and two base polygons with areas B_i and b_i. The plane equidistant from the base planes yields a cross section of area β_i. To the polyhedron we assign the number

$$\Sigma \frac{H_i}{6}(B_i + b_i + 4\beta_i).$$

This verifies α. It remains to verify properties β and γ.

Just as in section 35, we first examine the particular cases of β, namely, that of a slice that is the sum of two other slices with the same base planes and that of a slice that is the sum of two others possessing a common polygonal base and situated on opposite sides of it. Only the second case requires explanation. Verification results from a simple algebraic calculation when one has learned to calculate the area of a section of a slice (H, B, b, b_m) made by a plane parallel to the base plane and at distances of L and l from them $(H = L + l)$.

In the case in which $b = 0$ and $b_m = B/4$, this area is $(l/H)^2B$. If $B = 0$ and $b_m = b/4$, it is $(L/H)^2b$. If $B = b = b_m$, it is equal to B. Now, since a slice is the algebraic sum of tetrahedra whose four vertices are in the base planes, it is (see section 49) the algebraic sum of tetrahedra and triangular prisms, each of which appears in one of the three particular cases just listed.

The cross section of any slice is therefore given by the expression $\lambda B + \mu b + \nu b_m$ if λ, μ, and ν are chosen in such a way that this formula is applicable in the three particular cases considered:

$$\lambda + \frac{\nu}{4} = \left(\frac{l}{H}\right)^2; \qquad \mu + \nu = \left(\frac{L}{H}\right)^2; \qquad \lambda + \mu + \nu = 1.$$

From this, we have the formula

$$\frac{1}{H^2}\left[l(l - L)B + L(L - l)b + 4Llb_m\right].$$

The remainder of the verification is made algebraically.

The verification of β in the general case is derived as in section 35. The verification of γ similarly reduces to calculation of the number assigned to a tetrahedron, which is carried out just as in section 35.

53 *Pedagogy. Curved boundaries.* Thus, we finally have three expositions that are just like those made for areas. I repeat that I do not feel that these expositions should be adopted for classes. However, it seems to me that the study that we have just made might be recommended for future teachers as an example of efforts to increase understanding by bringing together fields of mathematics that we normally think of as being quite distinct, for example, elementary geometry and integral calculus. Such efforts may help them master the materials they will have to teach and ought to be required if we wish to train teachers instead of merely recruiting them.

The implications of this study for the classroom have been stated in section 40: avoid the traditional long-winded presentation and, above all, dare to state that volume has a definition and give it. This would, of course, be the first definition, sweetened as required. With this definition, one would evaluate the volumes of round bodies without incurring the serious reproach of section 42.

The presentation of this evaluation might be made as follows:

We have assigned a volume to bodies whose boundary is made up of plane and cylindrical surfaces, provided the cross sections of the cylinders belong to the family of plane curves each of which may be enclosed in squares the sum of whose areas can be made arbitrarily small. With the aid of these plane curves, we shall generate two new families of surfaces each of which can be enclosed in polyhedra the sum of whose volumes can be made arbitrarily small. The definition allows us to assign a volume to bodies bounded by these and the preceding surfaces.

Suppose that Γ is a curve of the type specified. It can be enclosed in squares C_i whose total area is less than ϵ; that is, Σ (area of C_i) $< \epsilon$. Let us consider the portion of a conical surface bounded by Γ and a point S on the cone with vertex S and directrix Γ. Suppose that H is the distance from S to the plane of Γ. This portion of the surface is enclosed in pyramids of which S is the apex and the C_i are the bases. The sum of their volumes is

$$\frac{H}{3} \Sigma \text{ (area of } C_i) < \frac{\epsilon H}{3}.$$

Thus, the conical surface in question possesses the desired property.

Let us rotate Γ around an axis in its plane that does not cross Γ. We may assume that the axis does not cross the C_i and that the C_i have sides parallel to the axis. Suppose then that h_i is the side of C_i and that R_i is the distance from its center to the axis. C_i generates a cylindrical body whose base is a circular annulus, so that the sum of the volumes of these bodies is

$$\Sigma h_i \pi \left[\left(R_i + \frac{h_i}{2} \right)^2 - \left(R_i - \frac{h_i}{2} \right)^2 \right] = 2\pi \Sigma R_i h_i^2$$
$$= 2\pi \Sigma \left[R_i \text{ (area of } C_i) \right] < 2\pi R \epsilon,$$

if R is taken greater than all the R_i. Thus, we conclude that the generated *solid of revolution has a volume.* The classical volumes are then deduced. Of course, the form in which they are usually given should be modified so that the statements do not rely on the concept of area of curved surfaces, a notion that is not yet clarified. But this is the only modification that needs to be made, and the proof will acquire a validity that is completely lacking in the usual exposition.

54 *Critique of numerical calculations.* In the present chapter, it has so far been only a matter of technique. For other matters I could refer to the corresponding sections in the chapter on areas. However, there is an objection that might be made for both quadratures and cubatures and that we do need to discuss: *Since it is only a matter of defining and obtaining numbers, should we not give a larger place to calculation?*

In Chapter I, I said that integers were only material symbols intended to give reports of physical counting experiences and that it was puerile not to dare to exhibit or write these symbols. In Chapter II, I said that all numbers were merely symbols whose purpose was to give reports of physical observations, geometrically schematized, it is true, but in such a way that one can almost say that the operation has not been schematized and that it is only the objects to which it applies that have been schematized: Instead of placing a wooden meter on a wall that is to be measured, we have put a unit segment on a segment that is to be measured. I said that one should not be afraid of writing these numbers or of calculating with them instead of confining oneself to the algebraic indication of calculations that are imagined but not performed.

Then, in Chapters III and IV, I stated that areas and volumes are nothing but these same numbers, these same symbols, but used as reports of other operations; namely, the operations of quadrature and cubature. Why have I so often reasoned upon numbers in these chapters instead of writing them and actually performing operations? By so doing have I not contradicted myself? Why did I not calculate the numbers n_i and N_i?

Theoretically, one single calculation would suffice to give all the theory of the areas of polygons: the calculation of the area of a triangle in any position whatsoever with respect to the grid T of squares that serves for the definition of area. And a single calculation, namely, the calculation of the volume of an arbitrary tetrahedron, would give the entire theory of volumes of polyhedra. This is true because it follows from the existence of the area of a triangle that line segments can be used to bound domains that have areas and hence that every polygon has an area. This proposition was the subject of section 26. Just as in section 27, it follows from this that the area of a polygon formed by the union of other polygons is equal to the sum of the areas of the component polygons. Then, section 29, in which it was proven that two congruent polygons have the same area, would be replaced with the proof that the area calculated for a triangle in any position is independent of that position.

The simplification that would result from this last point is apparent. The other two would not provide any simplification since it would be necessary to give the same explanations to the students whether one starts from the calculations of the areas of certain rectangles, as we have done, or from the calculation of the areas of triangles. Furthermore, the evaluation of areas would be obtained in different ways. However, the classical procedures that we have employed are quite simple, and actual calculation of the numbers n_i and N_i, while assumed mathematically possible, would be completely impossible pedagogically. Let us examine this calculation.

In section 25, I might have presented the calculation of the area of a rectangle with sides parallel to the sides of the squares of the grid T in a manner that would be more numerical and more in conformity with the exposition that I advocated in Chapters I and II by saying: "Let us evaluate the numbers n_i and N_i for the rectangle placed as described and having two opposite vertices with coordinates $(\sqrt{2}, \sqrt{3})$ and $(\sqrt{5}, \sqrt{7})$, that is, at $(1.41 \ldots, 1.73 \ldots)$ and $(2.23 \ldots, 2.64 \ldots)$. The squares U_1 which contribute to n_1 are those whose points have abscissas between 1.5 and 2.2 and ordinates between 1.8 and 2.6. There are $7 \times 8 = n_1$ of them. Similarly, those contributing to N_1 have abscissas between 1.4 and 2.3 and ordinates between 1.7 and 2.7. Hence, $N_1 = 9 \times 10$.

The method of presentation thus outlined might possibly be more suitable than the one given in section 25 for very young pupils; but, for such pupils, a logically complete exposition of the theory of areas would be out of the question. This is why I preferred the exposition given in section 25, which enabled me to speak in section 44 of the volumes of cylinders, whereas the more numerical presentation would have enabled me to speak only of certain rectangular parallelepipeds.

As soon as it is no longer a matter of the simple case of rectangles or special rectangular parallelepipeds placed in a convenient position with relation to the grid T, the calculation of the n_i and the N_i is, at least in practice, impossible even when one is addressing university students. Suppose that one is trying to calculate n_i and N_i for a triangle, two of whose vertices are at the points referred to and the third is at the point $(\sqrt{6}, \sqrt{8})$. It would be necessary, for example, to calculate the abscissas of the point at which the sides of this triangle intersect the lines containing the sides of the squares U_i and to take account of all the digits of these numbers! It is quite clear that one never calculates n_i and N_i but only values sufficiently close to be substituted for them in the definition of area. It is also clear that in the course of making these approximations, the area of the special rectangles considered in section 25 will show up, and that to calculate the abscissas it will be necessary to divide an arbitrary triangle by a line parallel to ωx, in short, that one will be led to arguments similar to those above.

55 *The essential abstractness of numbers.* The fact that it is necessary to discuss n_i and N_i without calculating their values may be an important observation. In spite of our desire to divorce metaphysics from mathematical considerations, we have nonetheless not succeeded in considering only the concrete. I stated above that geometric measurements were only physical operations applied to schematized objects. This is true of the procedure employed, but in its use there is an essential difference between the physical case and the geometrical case. The geometrical case requires an infinite repetition of the operation. A geometrical measurement begins physically, but it is achieved only metaphysically!

It would be futile to try to avoid this difficulty; it depends on the concept of a point. One arrives at this concept only by a mental operation that includes passage to the limit, and hence an infinite repetition. Every geometrical measurement is condemned to the use of this same repetition. To get rid of this, it would be necessary to renounce speaking of points and hence of numbers in general. It would be necessary, for example, to use that arithmetic of three-digit numbers to which Klein has referred several times, but which no one has ever constructed: An arithmetic in which three-digit numbers would not serve to write approximating values of numbers that are understood, but in which only three-digit numbers would actually exist.

Since this arithmetic does not exist, we have to do without it. Besides, we would also have to have an arithmetic of four-digit numbers, one of five-digit numbers, etc. in order to be able to express more and more precise physical measurements. The method man actually adopted, which employs numbers with an infinity of digits, seems both the most natural and the simplest. But a consequence of this is the fact that our ultimate aim in geometrical measurement is not the numbers obtained at the first or second stage of the measurement; it is the number at which we shall arrive only by an operation performed in the mind. The n_i and N_i thus have no significance in themselves, but are mere instruments to our final goal. It is legitimate to employ other more managable numbers if they can be found. We were right in not feeling obliged to calculate them; we were right to say that the measuring number was the final report of our operations although it does not furnish us in general with the numbers n_i and N_i. They have only a provisional value. If we start the measurement over with a different relative position of the region and the grid T, we get other numbers n_i and N_i. Similarly, two experimenters who arrive at the same value of a physical constant have not necessarily written down the same experimental numbers in the course of their operations.

56 *Reasoning and calculation.* To make precise what I said earlier and to avoid all misunderstanding, I have just made a long digression on one of the possible meanings of the question, "Should one not use more calculation?" A more usual interpretation of the question is the following: Is it proper to obtain the area of a triangle or the volume of a tetrahedron by considering neighboring domains, not necessarily made up of the U_i, whose areas or volumes result from formulas giving the sums of squares or cubes of whole numbers? We know this method quite well. It is used by some teachers in their classes. One may say that it merely complicates things for the triangle and that, for the tetrahedron, it has the advantage of dispensing with the comparison of two tetrahedra and makes it possible to reason in terms of only one tetrahedron. However, it does not in any way dispense with all the delicate part of the reasoning that confuses the students; namely, that dealing with the construction of neighboring domains and the passage to the limit. This method would be much more in agreement with the complete exposition outlined above than with the customary exposition. In a complete exposition, there would be no objection to obtaining the volume of a tetrahedron by summation.

I would not say as much if the course were intended for younger pupils. To calculate is to act and, therefore, children like calculation better than reasoning. They are willing to submit to the rules of calculation just as to the rules of any game. For a mathematician, to calculate is to reason; it means to analyze more profoundly the underlying geometrical facts. For a young pupil, to calculate means to leave to symbols the care of his reasoning; it means forgetting every geometrical fact in order to see only symbols. When both calculation and reasoning are involved (for example, in the question of the volume of a tetrahedron), the pupil does not doubt that he has given the perfect answer by writing on the blackboard the two or three necessary equations. It is of slight importance, in his opinion, that he has replaced the argumentation by gibberish.

If, as I believe, the purpose of mathematical instruction at the intermediate level is the development of the mind and not the acquisition of a technique or of mathematical knowledge, calculation should not play a great role in it. In more advanced teaching, which is intended for young people who have been taught to discuss geometrical, mechanical, or physical facts directly enough so that henceforth nothing could hide these facts from them, calculation will take its preponderant position.

57 *The introduction of integration.* These remarks would hardly be justified were I concerned only with the following, relatively unimportant question: Is this or that way better to calculate the volume of a tetrahedron? However, recently, a superintendent of primary education in France made the following suggestion: "Would it not be desirable to calculate areas and volumes by means of the formulas from integral calculus?"

I believe that his idea is the following: One would calculate the area of a rectangle or the volume of a rectangular parallelepiped in the usual method. One would consider this area and this volume as elementary concepts or concepts made sufficiently clear by certain allusions to covering a room with tile stones or the construction of a brick wall. Then one would show (what is already in the program of the French baccalaureate) that the area bounded by the x-axis, the ordinates a and X, and an arc of the curve $y = f(x)$, where $a < X$ and $f(x)$ is continuous and positive, is a function of X of which $f(X)$ is the derivative. One should prove an analogous property for volume, $f(x)$ being in this case the area of the cross section made by the plane with abscissa x, and one would apply these theorems to the area of a triangle or a circle and to the volumes of a pyramid, cylinder, cone, and sphere.

Let us see whether this procedure would, in conformity with the principles of section 18, be of most immediate use without sacrificing the educational values of the mathematics course. And first of all, among the children of 15 to 16 years of age who are receiving instruction at the intermediate level, how many will subsequently need to calculate areas or volumes? We may admit that all of them at some time or other in their lives will have occasion to estimate how many rolls of wallpaper will be needed to cover a wall or how many square meters of carpet will be needed for a floor. However, not one in one hundred will ever need to deal with anything other than rectangles and rectangular parallelepipeds, both of which are studied from the primary level onward. And not one in one thousand will ever need to establish a quadrature or cubature formula instead of using a formula established for him.

Therefore, the immediate utility is reduced to starting the study of integral calculus at the intermediary level on the basis that certain of the pupils, constituting a minority though an important one, will in subsequent study need to familiarize themselves with it.

58 *Disadvantages of the early use of calculus.*   But the study of areas and volumes has a higher utility which must be taken into consideration. It enables one to understand how, for practical purposes, people may have been led to develop geometry and how their effort is justified. It shows how people have been able to refine a commonplace concept by distinguishing it from closely related concepts, how they have made it precise by showing in relief the properties that characterize it, and how they have thus come to express it in logical terms, that is, to make it into a mathematical concept. No doubt, we do not think of that ourselves when we give this instruction, but if it is not justified by its practical utility, if it is not kept out of habit, it can only be for this cultural interest that it is required. And it is necessary because without it one would not establish any connection between those two mathematical pivots: point and number. Besides the definition of a number, that is, of the measure of length, one must also treat other measures to make felt the extraordinary precision that numbers bring to questions in which they are used. Numbers alone give confidence and sureness to the physicist. At the same time, it is necessary to make it understood that this power of a number is not a mysterious virtue but that it comes exclusively from efforts to analyze the concept studied in order to give it the precision of numbers. One should not believe that it is sufficient to say some hocus-pocus about an undefined or poorly defined number to make a question precise. The number comes last, to record, in a way, the progress that is attained.

No doubt also, our students profit very unequally from these cultural opportunities, each at his own intellectual level, and none would be ready to expound on the advantages that he has received from the study of areas of volumes. But is it not a great deal—and much better—that some of them are led by this study to similar efforts under new circumstances? And there are students capable of such efforts. One should not be surprised by this. Take an average student in the final high-school mathematics program who has received ordinary instruction without anyone having spoken to him of properties α, β, γ, and δ. Show him, by the procedures outlined in sections 31 or 35, for example, that these properties characterize areas. The pupil will be interested in the proofs, which are new to him, but he will tell you that he is already quite aware of the fact that is to be proven. In saying this, he will of course be mistaken, but his reply will prove at least that he has acquired an unconscious certainty of knowledge. There is nothing astonishing, therefore, in the fact that he will try again, when the occasion arises, to achieve a similar certainty.

The usual exposition, whether or not it actually states properties α, β, γ, and δ, rests so directly on these properties that it imprints them at least on the unconscious mind. This great advantage would, I fear, disappear entirely with an exposition based on integrals. The reason for this is not that the ordinary exposition says more about the origin of the concept than does the one based on integrals. A few words on tiling of floors or construction of bricks walls is not much; but it does make the student work with concepts in their most elementary form. It is by transposing triangles or tetrahedra, by decomposing solids into parts that are respectively equal or equivalent, that one becomes familiar with α, β, γ, and δ. Now in the exposition in terms of integrals, all this would disappear. All that would remain would be the filling of rectangles with squares and rectangular parallelepipeds with cubes. This would be too little to enable the student to grasp fully the importance of these characteristic properties.

59 *Difficulties with functions.* Add to this the fact that, as I have said, all the student's faculties of attention will be concentrated on calculations to the detriment of reasoning.

We can now make the following statement about this: Once again, take the same average student, who has profited so much from the ordinary exposition of areas and volumes and ask him to reproduce the proof that he is given of the classical theorem on the derivative of the area of certain regions.[1] The result will be frightful.

Why be surprised? It took centuries to see as inverses the concepts of integral and derivative, which were familiar from early antiquity in the form of area and tangent. Should we expect the poorest high-school student in his final year possessing no mathematical genius whatsoever, to understand this immediately and completely solely by virtue of the words that we utter in front of him, so that we can use this fact as the sole foundation of the edifice? This is having entirely too much faith in teaching, and I am amazed that an inspector general would have such illusions.

This is not the place to try to analyze the difficulties that may have stood in the way of our ancestors, but let us note nonetheless that, with regard to one point at least, our young students are in precisely the same intellectual state as the men of the seventeenth century. For them, the concept of function is confused with that of expression; or rather, there are two types of function for our students: the real ones, those found in problems [for example, $ax + bx^2 + c$, $(3x - 2)/(7 - 6x)$, etc. which have expressions], and those used in the *discussions* of the course [for example, $f(x)$, a ubiquitous notation that takes a precise meaning in applications, where it becomes $3 \cos x - 2$]. These latter are so unreal that one graphs *them* in order to give them a "mechanical" reality, as used to be said. And this graphing is pedagogically so necessary that in mechanics classes, where one is compelled to speak of functions that are not expressions, people in the second half of the nineteenth century acquired the habit of multiplying graphs, space curves, velocities, and accelerations and insisted on material means to pass from one of them to any of the others.

Very well; what troubles our students most in the discussion of the derivative of certain areas is the fact that in the process one considers a bad function $f(x)$, made concrete in the form of a curve, and that one proceeds to calculate an area on a yet worse function that is not made concrete by anything and that is completely unreal for them.[2] For the student, this involves a highly abstract reasoning; from our standpoint, on the contrary, there is nothing more concrete. To make ourselves

---

[1] The complete statement of this theorem is necessarily rather long. However, this does not sufficiently excuse the phrase that one used to find in the official French programs: the derivative of the area of a curve considered as a function of the abscissa.

[2] The phrase cited in the preceding footnote certainly does not provide the clarity that is missing.

understood, we use a figure and inequalities, which are effective for those who are capable of seeing, calculating, and reasoning all at the same time. But many prove incapable of this triple attention and, for them, the property one wishes to base the theory of areas of volumes on remains obscure and cloudy.

60 *Difficulties in justifying integration formulas for volumes.*   Perhaps it may be worth while in closing to point out a difficulty in the argument that permits application of integral calculus to cubature questions, a difficulty that certain textbook authors have been treating too lightly.

To simplify the calculation of the increase in area obtained by moving a straight line bounding the domain from the abscissa x to the abscissa $x + h$, one assumes freely that the function $f(x)$ defining the bounding curve constantly increases or constantly decreases from x to $x + h$. This restriction causes no hindrance since it is satisfied in all the practical cases and, in particular, the students believe it satisfied for sufficiently small h. Furthermore, failure to make any restrictive hypothesis on the continuous function $f(x)$ hardly makes the argument more complicated.

But suppose it is a matter of cubature. We have a solid whose cross sections made by planes parallel to *yoz* have an area $A(x)$, which is a continuous function of the abscissa x of the secant plane, and we wish to evaluate the volume of that part of the solid between the planes with abscissas x and $x + h$. This part is contained in a cylinder of altitude h whose cross section is the union of projections on *yoz* of the cross sections of the solid made by planes parallel to *yoz* with abscissa between x and $x + h$. It contains an analogous cylinder whose cross section is the part that is common to the projections referred to. One must prove that these two cross sections have areas that tend to $A(x)$ as h tends to zero. Now, this is not at all obvious, and it can be proven only if one makes more precise what one means by a solid. When such precision is reached, the reasoning is still by no means immediate even if one assumes the exposition developed at the beginning of this chapter. In other words, one cannot try to be rigorous without sacrificing generality in a mode of exposition that is intended to be simple and rapid. Thus, if, contrary to what I have always seen done, one wishes to be rigorous, it is necessary to introduce restrictions. The most natural restriction consists in supposing that, of any two cross sections parallel to *yoz*, one always contains the projection of the other. However, who does not see that restrictions of this nature to avoid considering the simple properties of volume call in question the existence of the volume itself?

61 *Formulas for sums and integration.*   I have postponed until this last section certain observations, only slightly relevant to my subject, in reply to an objection that is sometimes made to the calculation of the area of a triangle or the volume of a tetrahedron by means of sums of squares or cubes of integers: these sums are obtained only by artifices that the students learn by heart and that teach them nothing.

This is certainly true, but the objection relates only to the exposition that is ordinarily used. It could be avoided by a closer approach to the historical facts.

In the seventeenth century, mathematicians evaluated, especially for the calculation of areas and volumes, sums of terms u_1, u_2, . . . that were given as a function of their subscript, and this prepared and made possible the invention of infinitesimal calculus. The procedures that they employed have quite different appearances, but one can see afterwards that they all proceed in the following manner. The sums to be calculated are:

$$s_1 = u_1, \quad s_2 = u_1 + u_2, \quad \cdots s_p = u_1 + u_2 + \cdots + u_p, \quad \cdots . \quad (1)$$

Thus, we have $s_p - s_{p-1} = u_p$ for every value of p greater than 1. Now suppose that we have found (by what means is immaterial) a function σ_p of p such that, for every p greater than 1,

$$\sigma_p - \sigma_{p-1} = u_p. \quad (2)$$

Thus, $s_n = u_1 + (\sigma_2 - \sigma_1) + (\sigma_3 - \sigma_2) + \cdots + (\sigma_n - \sigma_{n-1}) = \sigma_n - \sigma_1 + u_1$.

Calculation of the sums (1) therefore reduces to finding a σ_p that will satisfy equation (2).

Let us make this precise. What we wish is an *expression* σ_p, algebraic or trigonometric, involving p that satisfies (2) when u_p is given. Thus, we are in the position of a workman who is asked if he has a tool for some task. He looks over the tools in his toolbox to see if one of them is suitable. This survey is easy and rapid for him if he already knows just what each of his tools can do, that is, if he has already made an inventory of the possibilities that his set of tools affords him.

Let us proceed like this workman and ask ourselves what the u_p are that the various expressions of p provide for us and that we know how to manipulate when they are inserted in place of σ_p in equation (2). If we do this, we will have made an inventory of the summations that we can carry out.

It is not necessary to explain how, by starting with a polynomial σ_p, one can get the u_p that are polynomials (from which, in particular, we get the summations necessary for the area of a triangle or the volume of a tetrahedron), or, by starting with the σ_p of the form Aa^p, one arrives at geometrical progressions, or, by starting with $\sigma_p = A \cos(px + h)$, one arrives at summations of trigonometric expressions, etc.

It seems to me that this slight modification in the exposition changes the entire content of it. In the first place, the calculation in it appears to be at the service of common sense and logic, as if it were directed by them instead of being substituted for them and replacing them thanks to some mysterious power. Secondly, this exposition would prepare our students to understand, just as the men of the seventeenth century were prepared to understand and to discover, the procedures for evaluation of indefinite integrals and the relationship between integration and differentiation, operations which are respectively the limits of the calculation of the s's from the u's and of the u's from the σ's.

V

LENGTHS OF CURVES.
AREAS OF SURFACES

62 *Introduction and historical remarks.* Works on elementary geometry are confined to the evaluation of the limit of the lengths of certain polygons inscribed in or circumscribed about a circle, to the evaluation of the limit of areas of prisms and pyramids inscribed in a cylinder or a cone of revolution, and to the area of the surfaces of certain solids approximating a sphere. No general definition is given, so that the objections of sections 42 and 53 can be made, for example, against the evaluation of areas of the simplest surfaces made up of portions of spheres, cylinders, and cones if they are not exactly the ones in the manuals for which a definition has been given explicitly or implicitly.

All this is therefore very trivial. It has been retained because the concepts of length of a curve and area of a surface are among the most ancient and the evaluations of lengths and areas were extensively studied by geometers and prepared the way for the discovery of infinitesimal calculus.

The practical importance of these concepts and the historic role which they have played in the development of science compel us, therefore, to keep this chapter, but it should be rewritten and not merely improved, as was the case for the preceding chapters. The content of those chapters was fixed by tradition; one only needed to concern oneself with the methods of demonstration and presentation. Here even the content of the present chapter is to be determined. Now this content necessarily depends on the importance given to mathematics in classes and in the examination programs. Hence, this is not going to be a chapter for intermediate instruction. However, it is possible to treat lengths and areas in it since what needs to be said on that subject is to be determined as much for the upper as for the secondary level. To be sure, integrals, simple and double, in rectangular or polar coordinates, are evaluated in many courses at the upper level, but questions of definition, in fact everything touching on geometry, is often evaded.

It sometimes happens in France that all a teacher will say is: The function $s(t)$ defined by the equation

$$s'^2 = x'^2 + y'^2 + z'^2$$

is called the length of a curve given in rectangular coordinates by $x(t)$, $y(t)$, and $z(t)$; and the trick is done!

Therefore, I shall examine the question without going into what one might say at the middle level and what should be reserved for older students. Besides, I shall confine myself to clarifying the concepts.

63 *Cauchy's reduction to algebra.* First, a brief historical summary will indicate the difficulties to be avoided and the necessity of certain precautions.

For the ancients, the concepts of length, area, and volume were fundamental notions, clear in themselves without logical definitions. The axioms (almost all implicit) that they used to make evaluations were not, in their eyes, definitions of these concepts. With them, it was always a matter of the room occupied in space by a line, surface, or solid. The difficulty began only when an attempt was made to measure that room, to assign it a number, and this difficulty consists entirely in the existence of irrational numbers. From this stem the aversion for numbers, the effort to avoid using them as long as possible, and the strange tricks employed to present them, which have already been mentioned, for example, in sections 14 and 20.

Cauchy was the first to provide a logical definition of these concepts. He did so incidentally and, in a way, without wishing to do so.

The reader has seen in the two preceding chapters how one can elucidate the concept of area of a plane region and of the volume of a solid by ridding them of their metaphysical meaning, in considering them as numbers, and in constructing these numbers by an infinite repetition of the same operations that were formerly considered as providing approximate measures of areas and volumes by means of axioms and postulates that were not explicitly stated and whose explicit statement or proof provide the desired logical definition. We know that Cauchy constructed the definite integral of continuous functions by an analogous procedure and thus demonstrated the existence of primitive functions.

In doing so, Cauchy not only defined the area of a plane region and the volume of a solid in a logical manner, but since he gave a logical definition of $\int \sqrt{x'^2 + y'^2 + z'^2}\, dt$ and $\iint \sqrt{1 + p^2 + q^2}\, dx\, dy$, he introduced the way of defining length that I referred to in section 62 and he suggested an analogous definition for area.

From a logical point of view, the question has been dealt with completely. Let us determine just what has been attained.

It is often said that Descartes (one should at least add Fermat's name to that of Descartes) reduced geometry to algebra. However, this was not true as long as it was necessary to appeal to the geometric concepts of length, area, and volume. It is only after Cauchy that geometrical concepts were made to depend on operations of calculation. Then geometry was indeed reduced to algebra; that is, since a number in general results from the measure of a length (see Chapter II), *plane and solid geometry have been reduced to the geometry of a straight line.*

To arrive at this so-called *arithmetization,* of geometry, it only remained to define a number in general, beginning with the integers without reference to measure or operations made on a straight line. This is made possible by the use of cuts, that is, by using once again Cauchy's procedure, which consists in taking as a definition the very operations that make possible the approximate evaluation of the number to be defined. For, as has already been stated, defining a cut is nothing but stating in abstract terms the results of a measurement of length.

64 *Limits of polygons and polyhedra.*   We have just arrived at the most abstract, the most purely logical form of exposition by constant use of this sort of reversal that Cauchy first used. And yet, neither the geometer, who would like to understand the geometrical relations between lines, surfaces, or solids to their lengths, areas, or volumes, nor the physicist, who would like to know why it is necessary to liken physical lengths, areas, and volumes to some integrals instead of others, is satisfied. Further study is required.

The first results regarding curves and surfaces were all obtained as consequences of the opinion that a curve is a polygonal line with an infinite number of sides and that a surface is a polyhedral figure with an infinite number of faces. The polygonal lines approximating a curve that one thinks of first are the inscribed and circumscribed broken lines. According to Peano, the postulates admitted by Archimedes are equivalent to the following definition: The length of an arc of a convex plane curve is the common value of the least upper bound of the length of the inscribed polygonal lines and the greatest lower bound of the circumscribed ones. Archimedes thus used those equally primordial elements of the geometry of the ancients, the line and the point, in the same manner. He thought of the curve in terms of its two dualistic aspects, as a locus of points and as an envelope of lines.

We know that little by little the concept of a straight line became a secondary concept. It recaptured some of its autonomy only when people created coordinates of a line similar to the coordinate of a point and introduced the idea of duality. For the question with which we are concerned, this evolution is reflected in the extension of the concept of a curve to that of a trajectory: a curve is still a locus of points, but it is no longer necessarily an envelope of lines. One may still consider inscribed polygons, but no longer are there necessarily circumscribed polygons. In short, in the study of lengths one came to consider only inscribed polygonal lines, forgetting that they had been preferred only because of their simplicity and that they possess no especial virtue that commends them more than other approximating polygonal lines.

All mathematicians agreed that the length of a curve (the area of a surface) is the limit of the length of an inscribed polygonal line (of the area of an inscribed polyhedral surface) when the elements all tend to zero. And when study of these definitions brought out certain difficulties, mathematicians were quite upset.

In the case of curves, research was done primarily by L. Scheeffer and C. Jordan.[1] The limit that served as a definition of length always exists, in some sense or other, but it may be infinite. There are curves such that every arc, no matter how small, does not have a length or, if one prefers, it has an infinite length. This result was paradoxical in that it was contrary to the usual use of the word "small" and, for just that reason, necessitated specification and separation of concepts previously confused. However, this result could not be a catastrophe as was the analogous discovery by the Pythagorean geometers of a segment that for them had no length because for them fractions were the only numbers. The difficulty, if there is any difficulty, does not arise in the case of simple curves. One can always, by following a procedure that is inadvisable but often employed, declare that curves without length are not true curves. This puts them, at least momentarily, *outside the scope*

[1] This work led Jordan to the important concept of a function of bounded variation.

of mathematics and postpones their study until later, whereas it would have been impossible to put the diagonal of a square outside the scope of mathematics.

In the case of surfaces, a more disturbing result was found. Schwarz had occasion to think about the concept of the area of a surface in connection with his researches on the solid of maximum volume among all those solids of a given area. In a letter to Genocchi, he showed that the areas of polyhedral surfaces inscribed in a given surface do not have an upper bound. And this is true no matter how simple the surface is, even if it is a cylinder of revolution. The example of Schwarz comes to mind so naturally when one thinks about the matter that Peano in his turn obtained it almost simultaneously and other mathematicians rediscovered and published it later. Let us partition the lateral surface of a cylinder of revolution into m equal portions with planes drawn at right angles to the axis. In each circular cross section, let us inscribe a convex regular polygon of n sides in such a way that the half-planes passing through the axis and the vertices of each of these polygons are rotated by an angle of π/n as we go from one cross section to the next. Now, we consider the inscribed polyhedral surface formed by the isosceles triangles whose bases are the sides of these polygons and whose vertices are the vertices of the polygons inscribed in the adjacent cross sections. It is clear that we have a surface that approaches the cylinder as closely as we wish as n increases. It is also clear that the limit of the area of this polyhedral surface depends on the limit of n/m. Thus, one can arrange for this limit of the area not to exist or for it to exist and have some arbitrary value.

65 *The effect of the Schwarz paradox on surface area.* The geometric definition of the area of a surface was crumbling. This was no catastrophe since everyone agreed on the following point: the area is $\iint \sqrt{1 + p^2 + q^2} \, dx \, dy$ at least in the simpler cases. Here was an analytic definition to which one only needed to give geometric interpretations, and in fact they already possessed such interpretations. Before mathematicians knew of Schwarz' example, which showed the impossibility of keeping the accepted definition, the difficulties connected with that definition had revealed themselves to all those who had tried to treat it rigorously. Some thought it possible to restrict the family of inscribed polyhedra so as to be able to prove the existence of a limit of their areas. The area of a surface is the limit of the areas of the polyhedral surfaces inscribed in the surface when their faces become infinitely small in all dimensions *in such a way that the angles of these faces do not tend to zero*, as some said, or *in such a way that the angles that the faces make with the surface tend to zero*, according to others.

These restrictions, however, are artificial. Nothing proves that other simple restrictions would not yield a different limit. Of all these limits, one does not know which corresponds best to the physical concept of area. Also, mathematicians would like to have a definition of area with a wide applicability somewhat comparable to that of the definition of length studied by Scheeffer and Jordan. Other definitions have been thought up, especially by Peano and Hermite, but they are so far removed from the original form that area no longer even appears as the limit of the areas of polyhedra!

I shall shortly show that actually all the necessary mathematical facts were available to understand the agreement between the physical concept of area and the analytic formula on the one hand, and to satisfy the need of geometers for generality on the other. This came to be understood only gradually.

66 *A similar paradox for lengths.* If mathematicians had not been hypnotized by the word "inscribed," if they had not forgotten that inscribing had been chosen only as one way of approximating, they would have seen that the difficulty encountered for areas existed equally for curves. Now it was just this difference between curves and surfaces that was most shocking. Allow me to refer to my own recollections.

When I was a schoolboy, it was agreed in France, as I have said, that one could evaluate lengths, areas, and volumes by passing to the limit. Soon doubts began to appear in the textbooks. The students who had heard Schwarz' objections in Hermite's analysis course had now in their turn become teachers. Besides, everything then predisposed us to a critical analysis of concepts: researches on functions of a real variable and on sets, which people were beginning to consider, Tannery's teaching, which had aroused in many of his students the desire for complete comprehension or at least verbal precision. People began to doubt, sometimes without knowing what they doubted. For example, the determination of the area of a circle by means of the areas of the polygons that it contained or that contained it (see section 42) was confused with an argument about limits.

Formerly, when I was a schoolboy, the teachers and pupils had been satisfied with this reasoning by passage to the limit. However, it ceased to satisfy me when some of my schoolmates showed me, along about my fifteenth year, that one side of a triangle is equal to the sum of the other two and that $\pi = 2$. Suppose that ABC is an equilateral triangle and that D, E, and F are the midpoints of BA, BC, and CA. The length of the broken line $BDEFC$ is $AB + AC$. If we repeat this procedure with the triangles DBE and FEC, we get a broken line of the same length made up of eight segments, etc. Now these broken lines have BC as their limit, and hence the limit of their lengths, that is, their common length $AB + AC$, is equal to BC. The reasoning with regard to π is analogous.

Nothing, absolutely nothing, distinguishes this reasoning from what we used to evaluate the circumference and area of a circle, the surface and volume of a cylinder, a cone, and a sphere. This result has been extremely instructive to me.

Besides, every paradox is highly instructive. In my opinion, the critical examination of paradoxes and the correction of erroneous reasoning should be standard exercises, frequently repeated at the secondary level.

The preceding example shows that passing to the limit for lengths, areas, or volumes requires justification, and, like Schwarz' example, it is enough to arouse all one's suspicions.

67 *Comment on the paradox.* Let us look further at this example. The measure of our broken saw-toothed lines which tend to BC is $AB + AC$; that is, it is any number whatever greater than BC. Thus, if we have a succession of polygonal lines tending to a curve $\mathcal{C}$ and if the length of these lines has a limit $\mathcal{L}$ as we operate on each segment of these lines as on BC, we get new lines the limit of whose lengths is any number that we choose greater than $\mathcal{L}$. *The limits of the length of polygonal lines tending to a curve $\mathcal{C}$ are all the numbers greater than or equal to some number $\mathcal{L}_0$.* It is for this reason that, when I needed a widely applicable definition of length and area, I proposed taking $\mathcal{L}_0$ for the length and the analogous number for the area. In a way, I was actually obliged to do this since $\mathcal{L}_0$ is the only number which, at first glance at least, is distinguished from all the other limits of lengths. Since it is sufficient to determine the set of limits of the lengths, this number is the complete report of the results of the search for these limits.

I do not have to examine these general definitions; they appear only after the physical concepts of length and area have been related to the analytical definitions, and it is this relation that should occupy our attention, since our present purpose is a pedagogical one.

68 *Physical concepts and analytic definitions.*   The length of a material curve is determined experimentally. For a number to be determined experimentally, it is necessary that the number itself vary only slightly when the experimental data vary slightly, since only approximate and never exact data are used. Therefore, it is necessary that the number be determined in some continuous manner by the data.

Let us try to make this more precise. The experimental determination is made according to some particular technique that, in the case of concepts that can be precise in terms of geometrical concepts, includes the setting up of apparatus, the measurement of distances and angles, etc. It is necessary that small errors in these positions and in these measurements entail only a slight variation in the result. The geometric definition is then obtained by stating the technique, but now giving to these operations the precise absolute character of geometry. If a geometrical definition does not provide us with a number that varies continuously with the data, it is incompatible with the experimental measuring procedure. It may in certain cases yield a translation of the practical concept, but this will have to be proven. It is a bad definition.

Let us examine the classical definition of length from this point of view. It has us take a polygon inscribed in a curve and increase indefinitely the number of its sides; that is, it has us take an ever increasing number of points on the curve. Now, if we try to apply this technique to a curve or to a segment *BC*, we shall have saw-toothed polygonal lines with vertices close to the curve or to *BC*. The more we increase the number of these points, the greater will be the error. True, the experimental technique includes prescriptions (perhaps transmitted only by an unexpressed tradition) limiting the number of vertices of the polygon according to the upper bound of the error that may be made in the position of these vertices. Thus, the classical definition is a poor one; that is, it is not the definition that actually translates the technique and that makes the agreement between theory and practice obvious. To obtain a good definition, we must examine the experimental technique more thoroughly.

The difficulty is that physicists have never had to make precise measurements, directly at any rate, of lengths of curves, and their technique has remained crude. It is only in geodesy that one finds precise measurements, but even there it is a matter of lengths of segments. Road measurements may possibly be the least imprecise. Let us examine the work of a surveyor measuring a road. If he put the two ends of the chain on different sides of the road, we should all agree that he is not proceeding correctly. Why?

In answer to this question, we would very likely first say that it is a matter of operating not on the band that is the road but on the curve followed by the center of the road. What is this center curve, and how does one obtain it? For example, if we take the midpoints of the perpendiculars to the two edges, it is an operation that assumes practical knowledge of the direction of the road. The technique will be based on the actual knowledge of the road with regard to its position and direction. No matter in what way we try to make precise the proper procedure for a surveyor, we arrive at the same conclusion.

How does a geodesist proceed when measuring the segment BC? He tries to make the points B and C as precise as possible. Then if he wishes to divide BC into two parts by a point D, he makes sure that D lies on BC by seeing that the directions BD and DC are the same. Thus, except for B and C, the geodesist obtains the positions of the points by determining directions in a fashion that specifically avoids considering BC as the limit of saw-tooth polygons.

Let us remember from all this that in practice one measures a curve by using one's knowledge of its points and its tangents and that this is done with the aid of polygons whose points approach those of the curve and whose sides approach the tangents to the curve. The practical method of measuring a curve will be explained if one shows that these polygons that approach the curve with regard to both position and direction have lengths that tend to a single limit as the approximation is continued indefinitely. The length is then defined in a logical manner as the value of that limit.

Now, this proof is immediate, just like the analogous one regarding areas, so that we have the definitions of length and area that we shall adopt. Thus, we return to the initial conception of Archimedes, who used curves and surfaces in their double dualistic aspect and to definitions that were suggested (see section 65) even before it was known that the approaching polygons (or polyhedrons) have lengths (or areas) that do not tend to any limit. The length that we define changes very little when the curve that we are measuring varies slightly in position or direction. The positions of the points on the curve and the directions of its tangents are the data on which the length depends continuously.

69 *Definitions and physical concepts.*   The considerations that have just led us to these conclusions are not the ones that led mathematicians to them. In fact, the ideas that have been guiding us seem to be in contradiction with the usual ones. We assume that a definition is subject to certain conditions and that there are good and bad definitions, whereas one repeatedly hears the statement that "definitions are free." I have never understood this statement. I know neither what freedom is meant nor the sense in which the word "definition" is being used. If it refers to terminology, everyone is indeed free to adopt the language that he chooses, sometimes at the risk of not being understood. If it refers to specification and if one maintains only that everyone may choose whatever he pleases as the subject of his meditations, of course, he may do so, though possibly with the penalty of being the only one interested in that subject and of making an effort that is useless for the development of the science. Be that as it may, for those of us who consider mathematics as an applied science, definitions are not free. At the very least, some definitions, those that are meant to make practical concepts more precise, are not free. For them, the obligation to avoid contradictions, which is understood in the adage cited, is not the only condition that must be satisfied. Indeed, it is the only condition if mathematics is nothing more than logic.

The path that mathematicians followed in arriving at the definitions of section 68 is quite different from the one that we have followed. They were not at all concerned about agreement between physical measure and the definitions in terms of the two classical integrals. Convinced that this agreement did exist, at least in simple cases, they did not seek the underlying reasons but studied the length number assigned to a curve (a function of the curve) and the area number assigned to a surface (a function of the surface). For this new type of function, for this new type of dependence, people naturally tried to find what became the concept of continuity.

Now, to simplify this, let us take the case of the plane curve $y = f(x)$

and a number assigned to it. It happens that some of these numbers vary little when $f(x)$ varies uniformly by a small amount. For example, if $|f - f_1| < \epsilon$ for every value of x, we have

$$\left| \int_a^b f(x) d(x) - \int_a^b f_1(x) d(x) \right| < \epsilon |b - a|.$$

Thus, $\int_a^b f(x)\, dx$ is such a number.

Other numbers, for example,

$$\int_a^b \sqrt{f^2(x) + f'^2(x)}\, dx,$$

vary only slightly if $f(x)$ on the one hand and $f'(x)$ on the other both vary uniformly little, though it would not be sufficient for just the first of these conditions to be satisfied. For other numbers, it will be sufficient if $f(x)$, $f'(x)$, and $f''(x)$ all vary uniformly little. Thus, mathematicians have been led to distinguish for the new functions, known as functionals, various types of continuity, known as continuity of the zeroth, first, second, etc. orders.

The length of a curve and the area of a surface defined by an integral involving only first derivatives are the prototypes of functionals with first-order but not zeroth-order continuity. And this fact, which is of supreme importance, explains the failure of the ancient definition of area and the success of the definition by inscribed polyhedra with faces only slightly inclined to the planes tangent to the surface. At the same time, this shows that it was not necessary to consider inscribed polyhedra; it is sufficient to have approximating polyhedra. In short, one is led to the definitions of the preceding section.

This also explains various facts that the reader may have noted. Length may be defined by consideration of inscribed polygons (this is the method of Scheeffer and Jordan), but one cannot define area in an analogous manner (here we have the Schwarz objection). The significant point is that if C is a curve with continuous tangent, if P is a polygon inscribed in C, and if AB is one of the sides of P, then the angle that AB makes with the tangent to C at any point of the arc AB (belonging to C) is less than the greatest angle made by two tangents at points belonging to the arc AB (from the theorem of finite increments if the curve is a plane curve, from a corollary of that theorem if it is a space curve). Thus, P approaches C arbitrarily closely with respect to both direction and position as the number of vertices of C increases without bound on the whole arc C.

In contrast, increasing the number of vertices of a polyhedron inscribed in a surface for every portion of that surface betters the approximation of the surface by the polyhedron as regards position but not as regards direction. Since the polyhedron has triangular faces, if we require that the angles in these faces not fall below a certain value, then increasing the number of vertices ensures approximation in both position and direction. This is easily verified. One definition of area referred to in section 65 is thus explained.

It has also been noted that a geodesist wishing to measure BC ascertains the positions of B and C; that is, he seeks to distinguish clearly the segment BC from other little different segments, but then what he seeks is to make the directions precise. The point is that for $f(x)$ and $f_1(x)$ to differ only very slightly in an interval (a, b) and for $f'(x)$ and $f_1'(x)$ also to differ only very slightly, it is sufficient that the second condition be satisfied and that $f(a)$ differ only very slightly from $f_1(a)$.

Everything confirms our conviction that the physical concepts of length and area apply to curves that are loci of points and envelopes of straight lines and to surfaces that are loci of points and envelopes of planes. Now that we understand these concepts better, we propose to expound them.

70 *First exposition. Curves.*   A first exposition would begin with a reference to certain practical problems that lead to the measure of lengths and that then make it possible to realize that men have been led to the physical concept: the length of a fence necessary to enclose a field, the weight of metal necessary for a stairway bannister, the number of loads of gravel necessary for repairing a road. To this should be added some remarks on the manner in which one makes these measurements in practice. In conclusion, one would give the logical definition. The curves with which we are concerned have continuously turning tangents at the point of contact. For such a curve, we shall say that a polygon is within ϵ of the position of the curve and is within η of its direction if it is possible to set up a one-to-one continuous correspondence between the points of the curve and those of the polygon in such a way that the distance between two corresponding points is less than ϵ and the tangents at these two points form an angle less than η. By angle of the tangents, we mean the angle between the directed tangents; by tangent at a point on a polygon, we mean the side passing through that point or, in the case of a vertex, each of the two sides that end at that point. The limit to which the lengths of the polygons approaching the curve tend as ϵ and η tend simultaneously to zero we shall call the *length of the curve.*

This definition requires proof of the existence of such a limit. Before giving this proof, I wish to remark that the precision in language that I have been using would be useless and even harmful in an exposition for young pupils. In such a case, one would sweeten the preceding definition by making clear without precise words the concept of a polygon approaching a curve in position and direction, and one would assume the existence of the limit, calling attention to the assumption. Then one would apply the definition to the circle. Here one would remark that inscribed regular polygons (or circumscribed regular polygons or both kinds, if one wishes) approach the curve in position and direction, and, since the relation

$$A = \tfrac{1}{2}L \times \text{apothem}$$

holds between the area A of such a polygon and its perimeter L, one would deduce

$$\text{area of circle} = (R/2) \times \text{circumference.}$$

There is no essential change from what has been done customarily. One would confine oneself to preparing for a more complete study to be made later when the students are more mature and will have more time to devote to mathematics.

71 *Existence of the arc length.*   Now let us prove the existence of the limit. Suppose that $ABC \ldots L$ is a polygon P inscribed in a curve Γ and that it extends from one end A of this curve to the other. Let Γ be partitioned into arcs AB, BC, $\ldots$. Let η_0 denote the maximum angle formed by two tangents to Γ at two points of the same arc AB, BC, $\ldots$. The angle η_0 tends to zero as the inscribed polygon approaches Γ.

Consider a polygon Π that approaches Γ. Suppose that α, β, $\ldots$, λ are points on this polygon corresponding to A, B, $\ldots L$. Consider one arc of Γ, let us say CD, and the corresponding portion $\gamma\delta$ of Π. This $\gamma\delta$ is a polygonal line. Each side makes an angle less than η with certain tangents to the arc CD if Π is within ϵ of Γ in position and within η of Γ in direction. Therefore, this side makes an angle less than $\eta + \eta_0$ with the chord CD. Suppose that P and Π are both sufficiently close to Γ so that $\eta + \eta_0$ is less than $\pi/3$. Then, the projections of the sides of $\gamma\delta$ onto CD

have all the same direction, and, since the projections of γ and δ are within ϵ of the points C and D, we have

$$CD - 2\epsilon \leq \text{length of } \gamma\delta \leq \frac{CD + 2\epsilon}{\cos(\eta + \eta_0)} < \frac{CD}{\cos(\eta + \eta_0)} + 4\epsilon.$$

Therefore,

$$\text{length of } P - 2n\epsilon \leq \text{length of } \Pi < \frac{\text{length of } P}{\cos(\eta + \eta_0)} + 4n\epsilon,$$

if n is the number of sides of P.

The numbers n, η_0, and the length of P are independent of ϵ and η. Therefore, the lengths of the polygons Π are bounded and those corresponding to ϵ and η all lie within the preceding limits, which differ by

$$\left[\frac{1}{\cos(\eta + \eta_0)} - 1\right] + 6n\epsilon.$$

The limit of this quantity, as ϵ and η tend to zero, is

$$\left[\frac{1}{\cos \eta_0} - 1\right].$$

This depends only on P. By choosing P so that the bracketed expression is small, we can have the value of this expression as close to zero as we wish, since the polygons P are themselves polygons Π (see section 69), and consequently the length of P is bounded.

Therefore, the lengths of the polygons Π differ from each other by as small an amount as we wish when ϵ and η are sufficiently small. In other words, the limit of the length of the polygons Π exists and is the same as the limit of the length of the polygons P.

72 *Translation into an integral.* Now that the definition has thus been justified, it is translated in the classical manner into the formula of integral calculus. Let us suppose that Γ is defined in rectangular coordinates by $x = x(t)$, $y = y(t)$, $z = z(t)$, that the three functions $x(t)$, $y(t)$, and $z(t)$ are continuous, and that the first derivatives are continuous in the interval (t_0, T) that we are considering. Suppose also that $x'(t)$, $y'(t)$, and $z'(t)$ do not all vanish simultaneously. Then, in (t_0, T), we have

$$|x'(t)| < M, \qquad |y'(t)| < M, \qquad |z'(t)| < M$$

and

$$\sqrt{x'(t)^2 + y'(t)^2 + z'(t)^2} > l,$$

where l and M are two suitably chosen positive numbers.

The length of a polygon P whose vertices are given by $t_0, t_1, t_2, \ldots t_n = T$ is

$$l(P) = \sum_{i=0}^{i=n-1} \sqrt{[x(t_{i+1}) - x(t_i)]^2 + [y(t_{i+1}) - y(t_i)]^2 + [z(t_{i+1}) - z(t_i)]^2},$$

which may be written

$$l(P) = \Sigma (t_{i+1} - t_i)\sqrt{\overline{x'(a_i)}^2 + \overline{y'(b_i)}^2 + \overline{z'(c_i)}^2},$$

where a_i, b_i, and c_i are suitably chosen numbers in the interval (t_i, t_{i+1}). Now, the difference

$$l(P) - \Sigma (t_{i+1} - t_i)\sqrt{\overline{x'(t_i)}^2 + \overline{y'(t_i)}^2 + \overline{z'(t_i)}^2}$$

can also be written

$$\Sigma (t_{i+1} - t_i) \times \frac{[\overline{x'(a_i)}^2 - \overline{x'(t_i)}^2] + [\overline{y'(b_i)}^2 - \overline{y'(t_i)}^2] + [\overline{z'(c_i)}^2 - \overline{z'(t_i)}^2]}{\sqrt{\overline{x'(a_i)}^2 + \overline{y'(b_i)}^2 + \overline{z'(c_i)}^2} + \sqrt{\overline{x'(t_i)}^2 + \overline{y'(t_i)}^2 + \overline{z'(t_i)}^2}}.$$

If in every interval (t_i, t_{i+1}), the derivatives $x'(t)$, $y'(t)$, and $z'(t)$ vary at most by ϵ, the bracketed expressions in the numerator of the above fraction are each less than $2M\epsilon$. The denominator is greater than $2l$. Therefore, the difference in question is bounded above by

$$\Sigma (t_{i+1} - t_i) \times \frac{6M\epsilon}{2l} = (T - t_0)\frac{M\epsilon}{l},$$

which goes to zero with ϵ. Therefore, the limit of $l(P)$ is the limit of

$$\Sigma (t_{i+1} - t_i)\sqrt{\overline{x'(t_i)}^2 + \overline{y'(t_i)}^2 + \overline{z'(t_i)}^2};$$

that is,

$$\int_{t_0}^{T} \sqrt{\overline{x'(t)}^2 + \overline{y'(t)}^2 + \overline{z'(t)}^2}\, dt.$$

73 *First exposition. Surface area.*   The only modification made for the case of length consists therefore in the statement of a definition and in the proof that this definition is logically acceptable. This is sufficient to prepare for the study of the areas, a study in which a new difficulty will appear, a sort of generalization of that encountered in the study of the area of plane regions: it was only to certain plane regions that we could assign an area.

Consider a surface Γ that has a continuously turning tangent plane at every point. We say that a polyhedron Π is within ϵ and η of Γ if a one-to-one bicontinuous correspondence can be set up between the points of Γ and Π such that the distance between any two corresponding points of Γ and Π is less than ϵ and the angle between the tangent planes at these two points is less than η. By tangent plane at a point of Π, we mean the plane or planes of the face or faces of Π to which this point belongs.

Consider a portion Δ of Γ. If the area of the corresponding portion of Π tends to a limit A as Π is made to vary in such a way that ϵ and η tend to zero, we say that Δ has an *area* equal to the number A.

In addressing young students, one would simplify the statement of this definition and would assume the existence of the polyhedra Π and the limit A for the surfaces Γ and the domains Δ that one would be dealing with. Then one would pass to applications to the surface areas of cylinders, cones of revolution, spheres, zones, and sections of zones.

For a cylinder or a cone of revolution, it would be sufficient to point out that a regular prism or regular pyramid inscribed in a cylinder or cone approaches the cylinder or cone in position and in direction.

Take, for example, the case of spherical domains and specifically the section of a zone generated by the circular arc AB rotating around its diameter $X'X$. Suppose that we partition AB into m equal parts by the points $C, D, \ldots K$. Consider the circles generated by $A, C, D, \ldots K, B$. Let us mark on these circles the points $A_1, A_2, \ldots A_n, C_1, C_2, \ldots C_n, \ldots B_n$ at which they meet the half-planes which pass through XX' and partition the section into n equal parts. Then we have the vertices of a polyhedron Π that approaches the surface in question with respect to both position and direction. The faces of this polyhedron Π are trapezoids such as $C_i C_{i+1} D_{i+1} D_i$ or possibly triangles, for which ϵ and η tend to zero as m and n increase without bound. Now, when n is sufficiently large, we have a number that differs as little as we wish from the sum of the areas generated by the sides of $AC \ldots KB$—hence the classical calculation.

Since the chapter on volumes precedes the one on areas of nonplanar domains, one may also return to a method already employed by the following argument: Suppose that we are required to find the area of a section of the zone of a cylinder or cone of revolution cut off by two planes P_1 and P_2 that are perpendicular to the axis, or of the zone of a sphere cut off by two parallel planes P_1 and P_2. Let us partition this zone into n equal zones by planes passing through its axis. Thus, one subzone is $ABB'A'$. In the case of a cylinder or cone, AB and $A'B'$ are two equal segments of generators. Let us pass tangent planes through these generators. These planes intersect each other along a line meeting P_1 and P_2 at α and β. We replace the small zone $ABB'A'$ by the two rectangles or trapezoids $AB\beta\alpha$ and $\alpha\beta B'A'$. As n increases, this polyhedral surface gets arbitrarily close to the original surface in both position and direction if a correspondence is established between the surface and the polyhedron with the aid of radii of the parallels of the cone or the cylinder.

In the case of the sphere, we again partition the zone $ABB'A'$ by planes parallel to P_1 and P_2 that partition AB into n equal arcs. If $CDEF$ is one of the subzones thus obtained, we draw planes tangent to the sphere at C, D, E, and F. Then from the center O of the sphere we project the sphere onto the tangent planes, taking for the projection of a point M on the sphere that point of intersection with the tangent planes that is closest to O. Thus, we have a polyhedral surface that approaches the sphere arbitrarily closely in both position and direction as n increases.

Now, in these three cases, if O is a point on the axis of the cylinder or cone or if it is the center of the sphere, the points of the segment joining O to the points of the polyhedral surface are the points of a solid made up of pyramids. The volume of this solid is v and it is connected with the area s of the polyhedral surface and the distance R from O to the tangent planes of the cylinder, cone, or sphere by the formula

$$v = \tfrac{1}{3}s \cdot R.$$

As n increases without bound, v tends to the volume V of the solid consisting of points of the segments joining O to the points of the section in question. Thus the surface S of this section is given by

$$V = \tfrac{1}{3}S \cdot R.$$

74 *Girard's theorem.*   In this formula, V is a number that we have learned to evaluate. Its calculation will take different forms, depending on what has been said in the chapter on volumes, but it will always be essentially the same. Pedagogically, there would be some advantage in postponing the actual calculations of V (and hence that of the volume of a sphere) until one has come to the solid that we have just considered. The calculation of the volume swept by a revolving triangle would thus become natural, and, furthermore, it is to this calculation that one would reduce the study that is often designated by the strange term "volumes of revolution."

If this part of the program were abridged to some slight extent, especially if we lightened the memory requirements of the pupils by not compelling them to learn by heart formulas that have never served any purpose other than passing examinations, and if we permitted them to remain ignorant (like every mathematician) of what a spherical segment or a spherical annulus is, we might find the time to deal with the area of a spherical triangle and consequently the areas of the portions of spheres bounded by arcs of great or small circles.

It is rather sad to say that young people who have acquired the degrees necessary to teach at the secondary level may never have heard of the magnificent theorem of Albert Girard. When they are introduced to this theorem, they always marvel at the beauty of the results and are amazed that no one has spoken to them sooner about a property that is absolutely necessary for a thorough understanding of Euclid's postulate.

The procedure followed here makes a slight modification in the usual presentation of Albert Girard's theorem by speaking about volumes first.

Consider three planes passing through the center of a sphere but not through the same diameter. These planes partition the sphere into eight spherical trihedra, the bases of which are eight spherical triangles which are pairwise symmetric about the common vertex. The volumes of these trihedra can be obtained with the aid of solids (like the one whose volume was denoted in the preceding section by v) made up of pyramids whose apexes are at O and whose base planes are tangent to the sphere. For such solids, $v = \frac{1}{3}sR$. Therefore, we have the following relation between the area S of a spherical triangle and the volume V of the corresponding spherical trihedron:

$$V = \tfrac{1}{3}SR.$$

Thus, two spherical triangles that are symmetric about the center of the sphere have the same area since the corresponding two symmetrical trihedra are the limits of symmetrical polyhedral solids that have the same volume. This being the case, we have four volumes, different in general, of the spherical trihedra V, V_1, V_2, and V_3 and four areas, also in general different, S, S_1, S_2, and S_3. If we note that these trihedra can be paired off to form spherical dihedra, then

$$V + V_2 = \frac{4}{3}\pi R^3 \cdot \frac{B}{2\pi}, \qquad V + V_3 = \frac{4}{3}\pi R^3 \cdot \frac{C}{2\pi},$$

$$V_2 + V_3 = \frac{4}{3}\pi R^3 \cdot \frac{\pi - A}{2\pi},$$

where A, B, and C are the three dihedral angles of the trihedron that cut off a volume V in the sphere, so that

$$V = \tfrac{1}{3}R^3(A + B + C - \pi),$$
$$S = R^2(A + B + C - \pi).$$

75 *Justification of the definition.*   Let us now return to the logical legitimation of the definition. The exposition that follows differs considerably from that of section 71. Now both the nature of the surface Γ containing the domain Δ and the nature of the boundary of Δ come into play. The precautions that need to be taken and the hypotheses to be made are most easily expressed in analytic language. It is an exposition that might be suitable in a course in integral calculus that we are going to give.

Suppose that Γ is a surface defined in rectangular coordinates by three functions $x(u, v)$, $y(u, v)$, and $z(u, v)$. We assume that x, y, and z and their first partial derivatives are continuous functions of u and v and we also assume that the parametric representation is nowhere singular, that is, that

$$(x'_u y'_v - x'_v y'_u)^2 + (y'_u z'_v - y'_v z'_u)^2 + (z'_u x'_v - z'_v x'_u)^2$$

does not vanish anywhere. Under these conditions, Γ has everywhere a continuously turning tangent plane.

We assume that the domain Δ obtained by varying the points with rectangular coordinates (u, v) in a domain δ belongs to the family of domains to which we have learned to assign an area; that is, we assume that the boundary of δ can be enclosed within polygons of arbitrarily small total area (see section 28). Let us partition the plane of (u, v) into squares by drawing equidistant parallels to the axes. Let h be the distance between two adjacent parallel lines. Let us partition each square with the diagonal parallel to $u + v = 0$. Let abc be a triangle obtained in this manner. To each point m of abc there corresponds a point M of Γ. These points form a curvilinear triangle ABC on Γ. We put in correspondence with m the point M' defined by

$$x = \frac{\alpha x_A + \beta x_B + \gamma x_C}{\alpha + \beta + \gamma}, \qquad y = \frac{\alpha y_A + \beta y_B + \gamma y_C}{\alpha + \beta + \gamma},$$

$$z = \frac{\alpha z_A + \beta z_B + \gamma z_C}{\alpha + \beta + \gamma},$$

where the u- and v-coordinates of m are given by

$$u = \frac{\alpha u_a + \beta u_b + \gamma u_c}{\alpha + \beta + \gamma}, \qquad v = \frac{\alpha v_a + \beta v_b + \gamma v_c}{\alpha + \beta + \gamma}.$$

This point describes the rectilinear triangle ABC when m describes abc. It is clear that the correspondence between M and M' is single-valued and continuous in both cases. These points M' thus describe a polyhedral surface P that is made up of triangles and is inscribed in Γ.

To Δ there corresponds a domain Δ' on P made up of triangles ABC and by parts of such triangles. Strictly speaking, Δ' is not a polyhedral surface. It would be easy to make a slight modification in Δ' so as to have a polyhedral surface in the strict sense of the word, but it is more expedient to expand the meaning of this word so that it will include a *surface* (that is, a locus of points in continuous correspondence with a plane domain) made up of portions of planes.

These portions of planes must have an area for us to be able to speak of the area of the polyhedral surface as the sum of the areas of these plane portions. This condition is satisfied by Δ' since the correspondence between abc and the rectilinear triangle ABC is a transformation in which each polygon in the plane abc and with area $\mathcal{a}$ becomes a polygon in the plane ABC of area

$$\mathcal{a} \times \frac{\text{area of } ABC}{\text{area of } abc}.$$

It immediately follows from this, just as in section 43, that to every part of abc of area $\mathcal{a}$ there corresponds a part of ABC possessing an area equal to

$$\mathcal{a} \times \frac{\text{area of } ABC}{\text{area of } abc}.$$

Let us now show that the numbers ϵ and η, which characterize the degree of approximation of Γ by P (or of Δ by Δ') with respect to position and direction, tend to zero as h tends to zero.

When m moves in abc, u and v can vary by at most h. Therefore, x, y, and z vary at most by a quantity $q(h)$ that tends to zero as h tends to zero. Therefore, the distance from a point M in the curvilinear triangle ABC to the point A, and the distance from a point M' in the rectilinear triangle ABC to the point A are at most $\sqrt{3}q(h)$. The distance MM' is at most $2\sqrt{3}q(h)$, and it tends to zero with h.

Each of the partial derivatives x'_u, x'_v, $\ldots$, z'_v remains less than a fixed number K in δ and varies by an amount less than $q_1(h)$ in abc. Therefore, each of the three expressions like $x'_u y'_v - x'_v y'_u$ varies by at most $4Kq_1(h) + 2q_1(h)^2 = q_2(h)$ when one takes the derivatives for some point or other of abc, a point that can differ not only from one expression to another but also in each expression from one derivative to another. Therefore, the various planes having the equation

$$X(y'_u z'_v - y'_v z'_u) + Y(z'_u x'_v - z'_v x'_u) + Z(x'_u y'_v - x'_v y'_u) = \text{const.}$$

make angles V with each other such that

$$\cos V = \frac{S(y'_u z'_v - y'_v z'_u)(\overline{y'_u z'_v} - \overline{y'_v z'_u})}{\sqrt{S(y'_u z'_v - y'_v z'_u)^2 \times S(\overline{y'_u z'_v} - \overline{y'_v z'_u})^2}},$$

and

$$\sin^2 V = \frac{S[(y'_u z'_v - y'_v z'_u)(\overline{z'_u x'_v} - \overline{z'_v x'_u}) - (\overline{y'_u z'_v} - \overline{y'_v z'_u})(z'_u x'_v - x'_u z'_v)]^2}{S(y'_u z'_v - y'_v z'_u)^2 \times S(\overline{y'_u z'_v} - \overline{y'_v z'_u})^2}.$$

Now, in this expression, the denominator exceeds any fixed number since the representation is regular, and each of the three bracketed expressions in the numerator is majorized by $4 \cdot 2K^2 \cdot q_2(h) + 2q_2(h)^2$. Therefore, the least upper bound η of V tends to zero with h. Now, the planes in question include, on the one hand, all the planes tangent to Γ at points of the curvilinear triangle ABC and, on the other, the plane ABC since the equation of the latter is

$$0 = \begin{vmatrix} X - x(u_0, v_0) & Y - y(u_0, v_0) & Z - z(u_0, v_0) \\ x(u_0 \pm h, v_0) - x(u_0, v_0) & y(u_0 \pm h, v_0) - y(u_0, v_0) & z(u_0 \pm h, v_0) - z(u_0, v_0) \\ x(u_0, v_0 \pm h) - x(u_0, v_0) & y(u_0, v_0 \pm h) - y(u_0, v_0) & z(u_0, v_0 \pm h) - z(u_0, v_0) \end{vmatrix},$$

where ab and ac are respectively parallel to the axes $v = 0$ and $u = 0$ and where the coordinates of a are u_0, v_0, so that the coordinates of b and c are $u_0 \pm h, v_0$ and $u_0, v_0 \pm h$. Transformation of the last two lines of the determinant by the mean value theorem yields the form of the equation in question.

Thus, we have proved *the existence of polyhedra possessing an area and approaching the surface arbitrarily closely with respect to position and direction.*

76   *Existence of area.*   It remains to prove that the area of the part $\mathfrak{D}$ of such a polyhedron Π corresponding to Δ tends to a limit as the numbers ϵ and η associated with π tend to zero. Consider one of the special polyhedra obtained in the preceding section, let us say P, and let ϵ_0 and η_0 be the numbers corresponding to it.

The calculation of ϵ_0 that we have made is very crude and can be made much more precise. With the coordinates stated for a, b, and c, we have

$$x_{M'} = x_A + \frac{\beta - \alpha}{\alpha + \beta + \gamma}(x_B - x_A) + \frac{\gamma - \alpha}{\alpha + \beta + \gamma}(x_C - x_A)$$

$$= x_A \pm \frac{\beta - \alpha}{\alpha + \beta + \gamma}hx_u' \pm \frac{\gamma - \alpha}{\alpha + \beta + \gamma}hx_v',$$

where x_u' and x_v' are taken, respectively, for a certain point of ab and a certain point of ac. Thus we have

$$x_M = x\left(u_0 \pm \frac{\beta - \alpha}{\alpha + \beta + \gamma}h, v_0 \pm \frac{\gamma - \alpha}{\alpha + \beta + \gamma}h\right)$$

$$= x_A \pm \frac{\beta - \alpha}{\alpha + \beta + \gamma}hx_u' \pm \frac{\gamma - \alpha}{\alpha + \beta + \gamma}hx_v',$$

where x_u' and x_v' are now taken for a certain point in the triangle abc. Hence,

$$|x_M - x_{M'}| = h\left|\frac{\beta - \alpha}{\alpha + \beta + \gamma}\delta(x_u') + \frac{\gamma - \alpha}{\alpha + \beta + \gamma}\delta(x_v')\right|,$$

where $\delta(x_u')$ and $\delta(x_v')$ are at most equal to the least upper bound $\lambda(h)$ of the variation of one of the six partial derivatives $x_u', \ldots z_v'$ when u and v vary by at most h. The coefficients of $\delta(x_u')$ and $\delta(x_v')$ are in absolute value at most equal to 1. Therefore,

$$|x_M - x_{M'}| \leq 2h\lambda(h) \qquad MM' \leq 2\sqrt{3}h\lambda(h) = \epsilon_0.$$

Thus, not only does ϵ_0 approach zero with h, but even the ratio of ϵ_0 to h approaches zero because $\lambda(h)$ tends to zero with h. This point is essential. It will enable us to argue as in section 72.

Suppose first that δ is made up of a certain number of squares of side H in a grid and that the squares of side h result from subdivision of the first squares. Then, Δ' is made up only of whole triangles ABC. To such a triangle, there corresponds on Π a region $\mathcal{R}$ made up of entire faces of Π and portions of faces. The plane of one of these faces or portions of faces, when oriented according to a chosen orientation on Γ, makes with the plane ABC, oriented in the same way, an angle that is at most equal to $\eta + \eta_0$ since they make at most angles η and η_0 with any single oriented tangent plane to Γ. If $\eta + \eta_0$ is less than a right angle, the orthogonal projections of these faces and portions of faces onto ABC will not overlap. They will cover all ABC except possibly certain points that are less than $\epsilon + \epsilon_0$ from the exterior of ABC. They are contained in the triangle ABC augmented by points that are less than $\epsilon + \epsilon_0$ from the interior of ABC. Therefore, one can find in $\mathcal{R}$ a polygonal region $\mathcal{R}_1$

such that the area of $\mathcal{R}_1 > ABC - (\epsilon + \epsilon_0) \times$ perimeter of ABC, and one can find on Π a polygonal region $\mathcal{R}_2$ containing $\mathcal{R}$ such that

$$\text{area } \mathcal{R}_2 \leq \frac{\text{area } ABC + (\epsilon + \epsilon_0) + \text{perimeter of } ABC + \omega}{\cos(\eta + \eta_0)}$$

for arbitrarily small $\omega > 0$.

Let us apply this to each region $\mathcal{R}$, keeping in mind the fact that, although it was not certain that $\mathcal{R}$ has an area, we know, by hypothesis, that $\mathfrak{D}$, formed by the union of the $\mathcal{R}$, does have an area. We get

$$\text{area } \mathfrak{D} \geq \text{area } \Delta' - 2(\epsilon + \epsilon_0) \times \text{sum of lengths of sides of } \Delta,$$

$$\text{area } \mathfrak{D} \leq \frac{\text{area } \Delta' + 2(\epsilon + \epsilon_0) \times \text{sum of lengths of sides of } \Delta}{\cos(\eta + \eta_0)}.$$

As ϵ and η tend to zero, the difference between these two bounds tends to

$$2\epsilon_0 \times \text{sum of lengths of sides of } \Delta \times \left(\frac{1}{\cos \eta_0} + 1\right).$$

Now, this expression depends only on P, and we shall see that it tends to zero with h. If δ is contained in a square of side pH, there are at most $2(pH/h)^2$ triangles abc. One side of this triangle yields an arc of Γ. If ab and ac are parallel to $v = 0$ and $u = 0$, the lengths of the arcs AB and AC are at most $K\sqrt{3}h$, since K majorizes the six partial derivatives $x'_u, \ldots, z'_v$. The side bc yields an arc BC whose length is at most $K\sqrt{6}h$ since the derivatives of x, y, and z in the direction bc are at most equal to $K\sqrt{2}$. Therefore, the perimeter of the plane triangle ABC is at most $4K\sqrt{3}h$. This enables us to majorize the preceding expression with

$$2\epsilon_0 \cdot 2 \left(\frac{pH}{h}\right)^2 \cdot 4K\sqrt{3}h \cdot \left(\frac{1}{\cos \eta_0} + 1\right)$$

which tends to zero with h.

Thus, *the existence of the limit of the areas of* $\mathfrak{D}$, *that is, the area of* Δ, *is proven under the hypothesis made for* δ. We shall return to an extension of this result to a larger class of domains δ. First, we shall seek an expression for the area of Δ.

77 *Integral formula for surface area.*   The area of ABC is

$$\tfrac{1}{2}\sqrt{[(Y_B - Y_A)(Z_C - Z_A) - (Y_C - Y_A)(Z_B - Z_A)]^2 + [Z, X]^2 + [X, Y]^2}.$$

The last two bracketed expressions are derived from the first by a circular permutation. Now, by means of the transformation that has already been used, this can be written

$$\tfrac{1}{2}h^2\sqrt{(y'_u z'_v - y'_v z'_u)^2 + (z'_u x'_v - z'_v x'_u)^2 + (x'_u y'_v - x'_v y'_u)^2},$$

if each partial derivative is taken at a convenient point of abc. If we use only the derivatives at the point a, this can also be written

$$\text{area of } abc \left\{ \sqrt{\left[\frac{D(y, z)}{D(u, v)}\right]_a^2 + \left[\frac{D(z, x)}{D(u, v)}\right]_a^2 + \left[\frac{D(x, y)}{D(u, v)}\right]_a^2} \right.$$
$$\left. + \theta[8K^2 q_2(h) + h q_2(h)^2]\sqrt{3} \right\},$$

where θ lies between -1 and $+1$.

As h tends to zero, the sum of the terms containing θ tends to zero because the sum of the areas abc is the finite area of δ. The sum of the other terms tend, by definition, to

$$\text{area of } \Delta = \int_\delta \int \sqrt{\left\{\left[\frac{D(y, z)}{D(u, v)}\right]^2 + \left[\frac{D(z, x)}{D(u, v)}\right]^2 + \left[\frac{D(x, y)}{D(u, v)}\right]^2\right\}} \, du \, dv.$$

However, this has been established only for special domains δ, which we shall call sums-of-squares. If it is assumed only that δ has an area, let us enclose δ in a sum-of-squares δ_2 and let us take a sum-of-squares δ_1 inside δ. We know that we can do this in such a way that the area of δ_2 minus the area of δ_1 will be as small as we choose.

To δ, δ_1, δ_2 there correspond on II parts $\mathfrak{D}$, $\mathfrak{D}_1$, $\mathfrak{D}_2$; on Γ, Δ, Δ_1, Δ_2; and on P, Δ', Δ'_1, Δ'_2. By hypothesis, $\mathfrak{D}$ has an area; Δ, Δ_1, Δ_2, Δ', Δ'_1, Δ'_2 have areas; we do not know whether $\mathfrak{D}_1$ and $\mathfrak{D}_2$ have areas or not. In section 76, we noted very carefully the point at which the hypothesis that $\mathfrak{D}$ has an area comes into play, namely, when one passes from the inequalities verified by the *area* $\mathfrak{R}_1$ and the *area* $\mathfrak{R}_2$ to the inequalities involving the *area* $\mathfrak{D}$. Arguing now with regard to $\mathfrak{D}_1$ and $\mathfrak{D}_2$, we must conclude that

$$\text{area } \overline{\mathfrak{D}}_1 > \text{area } \Delta'_1 - 2(\epsilon + \epsilon_0) \times \text{total length of the sides of } \Delta'_1,$$

where $\overline{\mathfrak{D}}_1$ denotes a polygonal domain on II containing $\mathfrak{D}_1$, and that

$$\text{area } \underline{\mathfrak{D}}_2 < \frac{\text{area } \Delta'_2 + 2(\epsilon + \epsilon_0) \times \text{total length of the sides of } \Delta'_2}{\cos(\eta + \eta_0)},$$

where $\underline{\mathfrak{D}}_2$ denotes a polygonal domain on II contained in $\mathfrak{D}_2$. Since $\mathfrak{D}$ is at the same time a domain $\overline{\mathfrak{D}}_1$ and a domain $\underline{\mathfrak{D}}_2$, the area of $\mathfrak{D}$ verifies the above two inequalities.

Thus, we have two bounds between which lies the number representing the *area* $\mathfrak{D}$. These two bounds depend not only on $\mathfrak{D}$ but also on the choices of P, δ_1, and δ_2. When $\mathfrak{D}$ varies in such a way that ϵ and η tend to zero, the difference between these bounds tends to

$$\frac{\text{area } \Delta_2}{\cos \eta_0} - \text{area } \Delta_1' + \zeta,$$

where ζ tends to zero with h. Therefore, if we let h tend to zero, the difference between the bounds tends to

$$\text{area } \Delta_2 - \text{area } \Delta_1 = \text{area } (\Delta_2 - \Delta_1).$$

The domain $\Delta_2 - \Delta_1$ corresponds to $\delta_2 - \delta_1$, which is a sum-of-squares. Hence,

area of $(\Delta_2 - \Delta_1)$

$$= \iint_{\delta_2 - \delta_1} \sqrt{\left\{ \left[\frac{D(y, z)}{D(u, v)}\right]^2 + \left[\frac{D(z, x)}{D(u, v)}\right]^2 + \left[\frac{D(x, y)}{D(u, v)}\right]^2 \right\}} \, du \, dv.$$

This is majorized by $2K^2\sqrt{3} \times area$ of $(\delta_2 - \delta_1)$. Since this last area can be taken as small as we wish, we see that the *area* of $\mathfrak{D}$ varies between these limits, which approach each other arbitrarily closely if we take ϵ and η sufficiently small. Therefore, the *area* of $\mathfrak{D}$ tends to a limit; that is, the area of Δ exists. Furthermore, with the choices indicated, the second members of the two inequalities have the same limit. From this, it follows that the expression for the *area* of Δ by an integral is valid for all domains δ having an area.

78 *Critique.*   The first exposition that I wished to describe is thus completed. No doubt, the reader feels that it is quite long and complicated even though it is restricted to the definition referred to as the least general. It might be shortened somewhat if one does not wish to bring out all the precautions that must be taken and it might be simplified by considering somewhat less extensive classes of surfaces and domains. But these modifications would be trivial.

This long and complicated exposition, while logically satisfactory, is physically or, we might say, humanly insufficient. It justifies only the procedures for measuring by means of approximating polygons or polyhedra, but not at all the use of the concepts of length and area in practice. In order to show that knowledge of the length of a road permits one to calculate the number of loads of gravel necessary for paving it, one must show how this length serves to calculate the approximate area of the road, hence the volume of gravel, and finally the number of loads. To explain how knowledge of the area of a dome makes it possible to calculate the weight of copper necessary to cover it, one must show how this surface serves for making an approximate calculation of the volume, and hence the weight, of copper.

Therefore, we need to add a few supplementary sections to the preceding exposition. However, these sections themselves constitute another exposition of the theory of lengths and areas—one that is shorter and more satisfactory, as we shall see.

This is not at all surprising. In section 68, I said that "physicists have never had to make precise measurements of the length of curves, at least not directly." In the indirect measurements to which I was alluding, one weighs a wire or a slab, a material image of the curve or surface that is to be measured. Thus, one determines length or area by a procedure consistent with the applications that one wishes to make of the result, which makes the applications legitimate. If we translate this new measuring procedure into words, we shall have a good definition since it will be in agreement with physical determination by weighing and with applications. And this definition is better than the preceding one because it is in agreement with the measuring procedure that is most commonly used in practice and that is most closely related to all applications.

At the present time, only one advantage can be mentioned in favor of the first exposition: it immediately justifies the use of the same words, "length" and "area," for arcs of curves and portions of surfaces as for segments of a straight line and plane domains. But it conforms better to our habits, and it is no doubt for that reason that it has been kept everywhere instead of the following simpler exposition, which was first suggested by the calculating procedures employed by Borchardt, procedures that were afterwards taken as actual definitions by Minkowski.

79 *Second exposition of length of plane curves.* Suppose that 300 loads of gravel were necessary to cover a road to a depth of 10 cm. Suppose that the middle portion of the road became rutted and that one wished to resurface a band in the middle of the road half the width of the road, again to a depth of 10 cm. One would naturally estimate that about 150 loads of gravel would be necessary. Since these two figures for the number of loads depend on the volumes of the cylinders occupied by the gravel when it is laid (cylinders of the same altitude whose cross sections are in one case the entire road and in the other the central strip), this estimation amounts to assuming that

$$\frac{S}{D} = \frac{S'}{D'},$$

where S and S' are the areas of the road and of the strip and the width D of the road is twice the width D' of the strip.

If we had $D = 3D''$, we would make an analogous assumption and, in practice, all these assumptions are in sufficient agreement with experience. Therefore, if the surface L corresponds to a width 1, the common value of these ratios will be L, and we shall have $S = L \cdot D$, $S' = L \cdot D'$, etc.

If the road is straight and of length l, the surfaces of area S, S', ... are rectangles, one side of which is equal to l, the other side being D, D', ... Thus, in this case, $L = l$. It is for this reason that the number L has been called the length of the road.

The equalities of which we have just been speaking are only approximate ones. The above explanations therefore do not possess precise logical validity. We shall transform them into mathematical definitions.

Consider a plane curve Γ possessing at each point a continuously turning tangent. Let us displace a segment of length $D = 2r$ in such a way that the midpoint describes Γ and in such a way that the segment itself is at all times normal to Γ. Let us assume that the curve Γ is such that, for sufficiently small r, the moving segment does not pass the same point twice. Let us denote by $A(r)$ the area swept by the segment, which we assume to exist. The limit of $A(r)/2r$ as r approaches zero, if it exists, is called the length of Γ. We show that, under very broad conditions, this limit exists.

If a curve Γ does not verify the above conditions but is made up of several curves Γ_1, Γ_2, ... placed end to end, each of which does satisfy these conditions (as is the case, for example, for a broken line), we denote by $A(r)$ the sum of the analogous areas relative to Γ_1, Γ_2, ..., and we apply the same definition. This amounts to saying that the length of Γ is the sum of the lengths of Γ_1, Γ_2, ... In particular, the length of a broken line is the sum of the lengths (in the ordinary sense of the word) of its sides.

Let us apply this definition to an arc of a circle of radius R and central angle α. The area $A(r)$ is that of the domain obtained by removing from the sector of radius $R + r$ and central angle α a sector of radius $R - r$ and the same central angle. Thus (see section 41),

$$\frac{A(r)}{2r} = \frac{\frac{1}{2}\alpha(R + r)^2 - \frac{1}{2}\alpha(R - r)^2}{2r} = \frac{2\alpha Rr}{2r} = \alpha R.$$

Thus, an arc of a circle has a length, which it is given by the formula $L = \alpha R$.

80 *Length of a space curve.*   In elementary geometry, one can confine oneself to a consideration of plane curves. However, if we seek to define the length of a space curve Γ, we assume that it verifies conditions analogous to those assumed above and we replace the moving segment of length $D = 2r$ with a moving circle of radius r whose center describes Γ and whose plane remains perpendicular to Γ. We let $V(r)$ denote the volume swept out and we call the limit of $V(r)/\pi r^2$ as r approaches zero (if this limit exists) the length of Γ. Just as before, we extend the definition to curves possessing certain angular points, and we deduce from it that the length of a broken line is, from this definition, the sum of the lengths (in the ordinary sense of the word) of these sides.

Again one can check that this definition is applicable in these more general cases and, furthermore, that when Γ is a plane curve, the two definitions yield the same number. Here is how one can prove the agreement of the two definitions.

Consider a plane curve Γ for which the ratio $A(r)/2r$ tends to L as r tends to zero. We decompose the side swept out by the moving circle of radius r into slices by drawing planes parallel to the plane of Γ at a distance h from each other. If two such planes bounding a slice cut the moving circle along chords of length $2r_1$ and $2r_2$, the slice lies within a cylinder of altitude h whose base is $A(r_1)$, and this slice contains a cylinder of the same altitude with base area equal to $A(r_2)$.

Since r_1 and r_2 are smaller than r, we have

$$A(r_1) = 2(L + \epsilon_1)r_1 \qquad A(r_2) = 2(L + \epsilon_2)r_2,$$

where ϵ_1 and ϵ_2 are bounded in absolute value by a number ϵ that tends to zero with r. The volumes of the two cylinders are obtained by multiplying by h. Therefore, we have

$$(L - \epsilon)\Sigma 2r_2 h < V(r) < (L + \epsilon)\Sigma 2r_1 h.$$

Now the sums appearing in the first and third members of this inequality are values that become arbitrarily close to the area πr^2 of the mobile circle as h tends to zero, one of them less and the other greater than this area. Therefore,

$$(L - \epsilon)\pi r^2 < V(r) < (L + \epsilon)\pi r^2,$$

where ϵ tends to zero with r. This proves the identity of the two definitions.[1]

It is also possible to prove this agreement indirectly by proving that each of the definitions of this paragraph agrees with the definition in terms of inscribed polygons in the more general cases, but I shall not go into that.

81 *Area of a surface.* After preliminaries similar to those for the length of an arc of a curve, we define the area of a surface as the limit as r approaches zero (which we assume to exist) of the ratio $V(r)/2r$, where $V(r)$ is the volume (which we also suppose to exist) of the solid made up of the segments of length $2r$ that are normal to the surface and whose midpoints are the points of the surface domain in question. This definition can be extended to surfaces having lines with angular points, and we conclude that a plane domain has an area according to the new definition if and only if it has an area according to the definition of Chapter III, that the two definitions are therefore in agreement, and that the area of a polyhedral surface is the sum of the areas of its faces.

This principle can easily be applied to a section of the lateral surface of a cylinder or cone of revolution or to a section of a spherical zone. All this is so simple, so immediate, so similar to the calculation in the case of a circle that I have nothing further to say.

82 *Analytical expressions.* In the course on integral calculus, after the definitions have been made as precise as necessary, they would be applied without hesitating to make simplifying assumptions. For example, suppose that Γ is a space curve whose regular representation in

---

[1] If we had wished to prove the identity only for the case of a circle, we could have applied Guldin's theorem or merely the particular case of this theorem dealing with a solid generated by a plane region possessing an axis of symmetry and rotating around a straight line in its plane that does not touch the region and that is parallel to the axis of symmetry.

rectangular coordinates is given by the functions $x(t)$, $y(t)$, and $z(t)$ and that these functions and their first two derivatives are continuous in (t_0, t_1). It is immediately verified that

$$\frac{y'}{\sqrt{x'^2 + y'^2}}, \qquad \frac{-x'}{\sqrt{x'^2 + y'^2}}, \qquad 0$$

and

$$\frac{x'z'}{\sqrt{x'^2 + y'^2}\,\sqrt{x'^2 + y'^2 + z'^2}}, \qquad \frac{y'z'}{\sqrt{x'^2 + y'^2}\,\sqrt{x'^2 + y'^2 + z'^2}},$$

$$\frac{-\sqrt{x'^2 + y'^2}}{\sqrt{x'^2 + y'^2 + z'^2}}$$

are the direction cosines of two orthogonal normals to Γ at the point (x, y, z).[1] Thus, $V(r)$ is the volume of the (solid) locus of the point

$$X = x + \frac{y'}{\sqrt{x'^2 + y'^2}}\,u + \frac{x'z'}{\sqrt{x'^2 + y'^2}\,\sqrt{x'^2 + y'^2 + z'^2}}\,v,$$

$$Y = y - \frac{x'}{\sqrt{x'^2 + y'^2}}\,v + \frac{y'z'}{\sqrt{x'^2 + y'^2}\,\sqrt{x'^2 + y'^2 + z'^2}}\,v,$$

$$Z = z - \frac{\sqrt{x'^2 + y'^2}}{\sqrt{x'^2 + y'^2 + z'^2}}\,v,$$

when the point (u, v) in rectangular coordinates describes a circle of radius r about the origin. Thus, we have

$$V(r) = \iiint \left| \frac{D(X, Y, Z)}{D(u, v, t)} \right| du\,dv\,dt.$$

To find the limit of $V(r)/\pi r^2$ as r approaches zero, it is sufficient to have the principal part of the infinitesimal $V(r)$. Now the functional determinant to be integrated is a polynomial in u and v, each monomial $c(t)u^\alpha v^\beta$ of which yields a term of the form

$$\int c(t)\,dt \cdot \iint u^\alpha v^\beta \,du\,dv,$$

where the second factor is a monomial in r of degree $\alpha + \beta + 2$. It is therefore sufficient to take the terms of the functional determinant of smaller degree in u and v. This yields

---

[1] This supposes however that $z' \neq 0$. If this is not the case, we partition Γ into arcs on each of which one of the derivatives x', y', or z' does not vanish. It is in order to be able to derive these direction cosines that we have assumed the existence of x'', y'' and z''.

$$\lim_{r \to 0} \frac{V(r)}{\pi r^2} = \int_{t_0}^{t_1} \begin{vmatrix} x' & \dfrac{y'}{\sqrt{x'^2 + y'^2}} & \dfrac{x'z'}{\sqrt{x'^2 + y'^2}\,\sqrt{x'^2 + y'^2 + z'^2}} \\[3ex] y' & -\dfrac{x'}{\sqrt{x'^2 + y'^2}} & \dfrac{y'z'}{\sqrt{x'^2 + y'^2}\,\sqrt{x'^2 + y'^2 + z'^2}} \\[3ex] z' & 0 & -\dfrac{\sqrt{x'^2 + y'^2}}{\sqrt{x'^2 + y'^2 + z'^2}} \end{vmatrix} dt$$

$$= \int_{t_0}^{t_1} \sqrt{x'^2 + y'^2 + z'^2}\, dt.$$

As a second example, suppose that Γ is a surface defined in rectangular coordinates by $x(u, v)$, $y(u, v)$, and $z(u, v)$. Suppose that these are continuous functions and that their first partial derivatives are continuous in a region of the uv-plane in which the parametric representation of Γ is regular. Suppose that δ is a domain in this portion of the uv-plane that possesses an area. For the domain Δ of Γ corresponding to δ, the points of the solid that we are considering are given by three formulas such as

$$X = x + \frac{D(y, z)}{D(u, v)} \times \frac{\rho}{\sqrt{\left[\dfrac{D(y, z)}{D(u, v)}\right]^2 + \left[\dfrac{D(z, x)}{D(u, v)}\right]^2 + \left[\dfrac{D(x, y)}{D(u, v)}\right]^2}},$$

where ρ varies from $-r$ to $+r$.

The functional determinant of X, Y, and Z with respect to u, v, and ρ, which has to be integrated to get $V(r)$, can be reduced to its principal part for finding the limit of $V(r)/2r$, so that

$$\text{area of } \Delta = \lim_{r \to 0} \frac{V(r)}{2r} = \iint_{\delta} \begin{vmatrix} x_u' & x_v' & \dfrac{D(y, z)}{D(u, v)} \\[2.5ex] y_u' & y_v' & \dfrac{D(z, x)}{D(u, v)} \\[2.5ex] z_u' & z_v' & \dfrac{D(x, y)}{D(u, v)} \end{vmatrix} \frac{du\, dv}{\sqrt{S\left[\dfrac{D(y, z)}{D(u, v)}\right]^2}}$$

$$= \iint_{\delta} \sqrt{\left[\frac{D(y, z)}{D(u, v)}\right]^2 + \left[\frac{D(z, x)}{D(u, v)}\right]^2 + \left[\frac{D(x, y)}{D(u, v)}\right]^2}\, du\, dv.$$

83 *Conclusions.*   Our second exposition is complete. The reader will not fail to note how much simpler and shorter it is than the first and that it is nonetheless, if not more complete, at least more appropriate for applications.

When one considers mathematics as a purely logical science, nothing can guide the search for definitions of area and length. These definitions are free. When we consider mathematics as an applied science, examination of techniques has led us to two good definitions since there are two techniques. The agreement of the calculations in sections 72 and 82, 77 and 82 explains the agreement of these techniques and shows that there is only one physical concept of length and only one concept of area.

However, it would have been possible to adopt a middle-ground by saying that mathematics does have experience as its origin but that it should be purely logical. Now a logical argument is based directly on properties and not directly on a construction. These constructions of length and area made in the preceding sections to reflect the measuring techniques would be advantageously replaced by *descriptive* definitions made by stating the properties imposed on length and area, which would be suggested by physical observation. In fact, this was done in the two preceding chapters when area (of plane domains) and volume were defined by means of properties α, β, and γ.

It will be noted then that the length and area that we have defined still possess properties α, β, γ but that these properties are no longer sufficient to characterize them. In other words, we no longer have property δ, which can be stated as follows: the number sought is defined up to a constant factor by α, β, γ. Suppose that to a curve or a surface we assign the indicatrix curve of the principal normals (or the binormals) or the indicatrix surface of the normals. The length of that curve or the area of that surface, thought of as assigned to the original curve or surface, still verifies α, β, γ. The observations that we have made lead us to state this new condition:

ϵ—When a curve (or surface) Π tends uniformly in position and direction to a fixed curve or surface Γ, where Π and Γ belong to the class of curves having a length (or to the class of surfaces having an area), the length (or area) of Π tends to the length or area of Γ.

Properties α, β, γ, ϵ are sufficient to imply δ if it is understood that every segment (or polygon) belongs to the family of curves possessing a length (or to the family of surfaces possessing an area). Then the length of every polygonal line (or the area of every polyhedral surface) can be deduced from it. Then ϵ leads to the definition of our first exposition, and it is, in fact, by that path that we were led to it.

This shows first that, from a logical point of view just as from the point of view of the critique of the concepts, the first definitions have certain advantages that we have not brought out, and second, that one should not omit them in the case of instruction more advanced than that of the elements of integral calculus.

VI

MEASURABLE MAGNITUDES

84 *Introduction.* The program of the first class at the secondary level, the sixth grade [see footnote, page 26], includes a chapter entitled "Measurement of magnitudes, concept of a fraction." The program of the last class at the secondary level, namely, the mathematics program, includes this same chapter, "Measurement of magnitudes." Between these two classes, the point of view ought to be quite different both because of the age of the students and because one needs to deal with the practical concept in the sixth grade and with the abstract concept in the mathematics program.

There is no problem for the material of the sixth grade. The children are taught what is a third, a fourth, three-fifths by cutting up small cakes. The children understand perfectly, and, in general, they are quite interested in this part of the instruction. On the other hand, in the mathematics program, the difficulties are considerable, so much so that the chapter is purely and simply shoved aside or it is replaced by exactly the prelogical point of view of the sixth grade.

It is, however, obvious that the chapter was thought a very important one. It is to that chapter that one usually refers when, for example, one passes from the comparison of the volumes of two rectangular parallelepipeds with two common dimensions to a comparison of two arbitrary rectangular parallelepipeds. It should, then, resolve the logical difficulties in preparation for all the applications. This chapter has been incorporated in the arithmetic program because of the extensions of the concept of number that are associated with it, but this association is made also because the arithmetic program is the most primitive and most purely logical of all the branches of mathematics if one wishes to give the chapter on the measurement of magnitudes a purely logical aspect. But then the question arises as to the logical definition of magnitudes. In practice, the teachers do not give any definition. They give examples of magnitudes (areas, volumes, weights, quantities of heat) and examples of concepts that are not magnitudes: velocities, temperatures, potentials, etc.

It is clear that this procedure (which, in the teaching of living languages, is known by the name of "the direct method") assumes that the concept of a magnitude is already acquired by everyday experience, by familiarity with physical phenomena, and by common sense and that the most that one can hope to do is to make the terminology known. The result is that when one turns from the chapter on volumes, for example, to the chapter on magnitudes in order to find the general explanations, one follows a vicious circle since the latter chapter explains magnitudes in general only by analogy with volumes. What then is the difficulty that must be overcome to make the concept of magnitude logically precise? It is entirely metaphysical and of the same nature as that encountered for the concept of a number. Just as we were urged not to confuse a number with the symbol that represents it, so we are advised to distinguish between a magnitude and the number measuring the magnitude, and even to use magnitude to broaden the concept of a number and to arrive at fractions and more general numbers. Thus, it is a matter of defining length, area, and volume, or, more exactly, a concept including length, area, and volume without speaking of numbers.

Thus, we have two attitudes: either one takes refuge in metaphysics or one starts over again and defines "equality," "sum," "product," etc., when the matter of magnitudes comes up. In short, one reconstructs the theory of numbers without daring to pronounce that word. This second attitude is well known. It is to it that I have several times referred. It is the attitude that shows up, for example, when one speaks of the ratio of two segments but treats that ratio as if it were not a number.

We have a very curious manifestation of the first attitude in this recommendation by that eminent geometer, G. Darboux, to the sharp, critical mind, J. Tannery: try to "extract everything that one can from the old definition that *a magnitude is everything that is susceptible of increase and decrease.*"

Thus, it would be necessary to create a theory that could be applied simultaneously to volumes and ambition, to temperature and one's appetite, to the national budget, to the fertility of the soil, to intelligence, to the level of the Seine, to astonishment, etc., and, in particular, to the magnitude of the number that measures a magnitude. It is enough to say that the real difficulty would consist in finding something that does *not* belong to the category of magnitude, something that is not in some way susceptible to either increase or decrease. For a study to be possible, it is necessary to restrict oneself. The word "magnitude" is certainly employed at the present time by mathematicians in very general and diverse senses. Every number is called a magnitude and, if that is not enough, in addition to these scalar magnitudes, there are other magnitudes of which vector magnitudes are the simplest. However, when one speaks of the theory of magnitudes, the word "magnitude" has a more restricted meaning. In order to avoid confusion, terminology such as "directly measurable magnitude" has been suggested, but one would have to make precise the application of such terminology.

85   *What is a measurable magnitude?*   We say in general that for there to be a directly measurable magnitude, we must be able to speak of equality and of addition. Mass is cited as an example because one can speak of two equal masses and of a mass that is the sum of two other masses. But temperatures are excluded because, while we may speak of equal temperatures, we do not speak of one temperature as being the sum of two other temperatures. Note that nothing would prevent us from talking about it, of saying that 30° and 40° make 70°, that whenever it is a matter of numbers, we may speak of equality and sums. What is meant is that the sum of two temperatures has no *physical* significance. But what *logical* importance can this statement have? Evidently none, and a logical definition of magnitudes should not be based on the physical significance of concepts in the present state of science. Furthermore, is it true that sums of temperature are without physical significance? Observe that when we speak of 40°C, we assign a temperature difference between a body and melting ice. Similarly, we use a temperature difference when we measure the elongation of a rail in the summertime over its temperature in the winter. And whoever uses differences uses sums in the very process. In fact, when we say that 40°C is the same as 313° absolute, we perform an addition of temperatures. Similarly, we add velocities (in the composition of two motions, for example); we subtract potentials (since we never use anything except potential differences), etc. In short, *the criterion indicated, which could have no logical content, has no meaning at all*. However, we shall find it again very soon but in a more precise form. The examination that we have just made proves in fact only one thing, namely, that the criterion is neither clearly conceived nor precisely stated. It does not prove that it is without foundation.

Since the difficulty was caused by the overly metaphysical attitude adopted, let us conclude from this critique that we should try the method that has proven successful in the case of numbers, lengths, areas, and volumes. We have renounced the distinction between the metaphysical number assigned to a collection and the symbol that represents it, between the metaphysical length and the metaphysical number that measures it, the symbol that represents that number, and similarly for areas and volumes. We have sought to define directly numbers used as symbols, the only ones that are important in mathematics, and we leave for others the problem of dealing with metaphysical problems which are outside our competence. And, since everyone agrees that lengths, areas, and volumes constitute perfect examples of magnitudes, we need primarily to seek what there is in common about what we have said regarding each of these concepts. This is what we propose to do, assuming, however, that the chapter on magnitudes in general comes after those on the lengths of segments, areas of polygons and volumes of polyhedra, or at least after some of them.

The concept that we shall make precise will not include all those to which the different meanings given to the word "magnitude" are applicable. We realize that we must set limits to our goal, which is not the greatest generality possible but merely an extension that does not diminish the importance that teachers intend at the present time to give to the chapter on the measurement of magnitudes.

86 *Definition of a magnitude assigned to bodies. First condition.* Let us examine what the different definitions in the preceding chapters have in common. Since physical masses are also considered as perfect examples of magnitude, we shall keep those characteristics they have in common that can be carried over to the case of masses. The length of a segment or of an arc of a circle, the area of a polygon or of a domain delimited in a surface, and the volume of a polyhedron or other solid have been defined as positive numbers assigned to geometrical entities and completely defined by these entities up to a choice of units. This is condition α. The case of masses leads us to state this first part of the definition, which will be composed of two parts, (a) and (b).

(a) *A magnitude G is said to be defined for the bodies belonging to a given family of bodies if, for each of them and for each portion of each of them, a definite positive number has been assigned.*

The reader will recall the procedure that made it possible to determine a number by giving a name to that number, to that magnitude: length, volume, mass, quantity of heat, etc. We also say that we have measured the length, volume, etc. The physical process of determination makes it possible to attain a number in actuality only up to a certain error. It never enables us to discriminate between one number and all the numbers that are extremely close to it. One may therefore imagine, as we have done in case of the procedure for measuring the length of a segment, that the procedure is infinitely perfectible to the point of leading to a single number that is completely determined.

This family of bodies will vary from one magnitude to another. All these bodies may be likened, depending on the case, to segments of a straight line, or to the arc of curves, or to surface domains, or to portions of space. In fact at the less elementary level, one may consider portions of spaces of more than three dimensions or of manifolds embedded in such spaces.

87 *Second condition.*   The case of masses shows that we may not expect to generalize condition (γ) of the preceding sections. To two geometrically equal bodies there may correspond two different numbers serving as measure of the magnitude G for these bodies. On the other hand, condition (β) can be generalized and it is essential:

(b) *If a body C is partitioned into a certain number of sub-bodies C_1, $C_2, \ldots, C_p$, and if for these bodies the magnitude G is g on the one hand and $g_1, g_2, \ldots, g_p$ on the other, we must have*

$$g = g_1 + g_2 + \cdots + g_p.$$

This condition makes precise the condition that we criticized above. It must be possible to speak of the sum of two magnitudes.

Up to now, we have left the word "body" with an imprecise character analogous to that given earlier to the word "domain." It is clear that in geometry or in theoretical physics, it will be possible to make precise the logical meaning given to that word. In geometry in particular, it is possible to give the word "body" a more or less broad meaning, for example, the meaning of set or figure. It will only be necessary in each case to define what we shall call a partition of the total figure into portions.

Furthermore, the magnitude may be assigned not to data of a geometric nature but to data of a more varied nature. Here, examination of geometrically similar bodies with domains delineated in space or on surfaces or on curves will be sufficient for us.

The family of these bodies is also subjected to a condition that can be left understood at the elementary level but one whose logical necessity will appear at the time of the proof of the one theorem that, with the definition stated, constitutes the entire theory of magnitudes.

88 *Proportionality condition.*   *Suppose that two magnitudes G and G_1 are defined for the same family of bodies. Suppose also that, for all bodies for which G has the same value g (whatever that value may be), G_1 has a single value g_1. Then, the relation*

$$g_1 = kg$$

holds between g and g_1, where k is a constant.

To show this property, let us compare the numbers g and g_1 assigned to a body C with numbers γ and γ_1 assigned to a body Γ chosen as a standard. For any integer n, let us determine the integer m such that

$$\frac{m}{n} \le \frac{g}{\gamma} < \frac{m+1}{n},$$

and let us partition the body C into m sub-bodies for which G has a single value g' and let us partition Γ into n sub-bodies for which G has a single value γ'. We then have

$$g = mg', \qquad \gamma = n\gamma', \qquad g' \ge \gamma',$$

where equality holds only when it held originally. When this is not the case, we can decrease each of the m sub-bodies that make up C in such a way as to obtain a body for which G has the value γ'. In other words, we can replace the m bodies constituting C by $2m$ bodies of which m each gives to G the value γ'. These last m bodies and the n bodies that constitute Γ all give G the same value γ'; they give to G_1 a single value γ_1', and we have

$$g_1 \ge m\gamma_1', \qquad \gamma_1 = n\gamma_1', \qquad g_1/\gamma_1 \ge m/n,$$

where equality holds only when it held originally.

If we apply this result to the relation

$$\frac{\gamma}{g} < \frac{n}{m+1},$$

we get

$$\frac{m}{n} \le \frac{g_1}{\gamma_1} < \frac{m+1}{n},$$

$$\left| \frac{g}{\gamma} - \frac{g_1}{\gamma_1} \right| < \frac{1}{n}.$$

And since n is any integer, we have

$$\frac{g_1}{g} = \frac{\gamma_1}{\gamma} = k.$$

89 *Third condition.* The theorem is proven. However, in the course of the proof, we used decompositions of bodies into sub-bodies, and the possibility of doing this does not follow from hypotheses (a) and (b). I do not believe that there is any drawback at all to making this supplementary hypothesis in the classroom without saying so explicitly. On the other hand, the teachers should note that (a) and (b) are logically insufficient.

The supplementary hypothesis could be formulated as follows:

(c) *The family of bodies for which a magnitude is defined must be sufficiently extensive for every body in the family to be reducible to a single point by successive reductions (without its leaving the family) in such a way that in the course of these reductions the magnitude decreases continuously from its original value to zero.*

It will be noted that, as far as area is concerned, plane polygons constitute such a family of bodies. It will also be noted that the larger family of domains that we have been calling measurable domains also satisfies condition (c) for the area magnitude. The necessity for a condition such as (c) thus appears in connection with the difficulties that have compelled us to restrict ourselves to certain domains for the study of area or volume.

90 *Comments on the conditions.* Another observation that teachers should make, although there is no need to make it explicit in class, is that condition (b) can be to some extent illusory. Consider a family of bodies F made up of the family F_1 of arcs of a circle C_1 and a family F_2 of arcs of a circle C_2, different from C_1. To the arcs of F_1, we assign their measure in the manner explained in the second book on geometry with the aid of a unit arc U_1 of C_1. To each of the arcs of F_2 we assign its measure with the aid of a unit arc U_2 of C_2. It will be correct to say that all these numbers constitute a magnitude defined for the bodies of the family F. In reality, however, we would then have two magnitudes defined respectively for the bodies of F_1 and for the bodies of F_2. Whenever a magnitude is defined for all the bodies of a family F and this family F can be partitioned into two disjoint families F_1 and F_2 such that each of them also contains the portions of the bodies belonging to F which it contains, condition (b) becomes illusory in the sense that it applies to F_1 and F_2 but not to F except by way of F_1 and F_2. If it is correct to say, for example, that the lengths of arcs of curves with continuous tangents are magnitudes assigned to these curves, we can make the content of (b) more explicit by saying that the lengths of various arcs of a curve with continuous tangents are magnitudes.

We note that these arbitrary choices of U_1 and U_2 might have been made in the preceding example even if the radii of C_1 and C_2 had been equal. When it is a matter of lengths in the sense of Chapter V and not a matter of measurements in the sense of the second book of the geometry course, the arcs U_1 and U_2 of the same length l are equal. We have, in effect, imposed condition (γ) on ourselves. With regard to *geometrical* magnitudes, that is, magnitudes satisfying condition (γ), conditions (b) and (γ) can be combined into the following statement: *The value G of the magnitude of a body C that can be partitioned into bodies that are respectively equal to bodies C_1, C_2, . . . C_p is the sum $g_1 + g_2 + \cdots + g_p$ of the values of the magnitude for C_1, C_2, . . . , C_p.*

If we like, we may agree to give new meanings to the words "partition a body." We may agree that C is partitioned into C_1, C_2, . . . , C_p or that C is the sum of these bodies and we may keep statement (b). Here is the origin of the extensions of the concept of magnitude, which I only point out and which can be obtained by giving the word "partition" new meanings. We may also agree that magnitude, instead of being a positive number, is any other mathematical entity for which addition may have been defined.

Examination of these generalizations takes me away from my program, but it was worthwhile to point them out in order to emphasize that the single concept involved here is voluntarily narrow.

Here are observations that should be called to the student's attention: The length of the altitude of a pyramid is not a magnitude assigned to the pyramid but is a magnitude assigned to the altitude segment. The area of the surface of a polyhedron is not a magnitude defined for the family of polyhedra, but the area of a portion of the surface of a polyhedron is a magnitude defined for portions of the surface that are treated as bodies. The altitude along ox of a rectangular parallelepiped with one edge parallel to ox is not a magnitude assigned to the polyhedron, but it would be if all polyhedra were intercepted by planes perpendicular to ox in a single infinite rectangular prism.

Thus, a number is or is not a magnitude depending on the body to which it is assigned. There is no necessary identity between the family of bodies for which it is defined and the family of those for which it is a magnitude.

91 *Proportional magnitudes.* *When two magnitudes satisfy the conditions of section 88 (that is, when they are defined for the same family of bodies) and when the value of one of them g determines the other g_1, the magnitudes are said to be proportional.*

The theorem that we have proven shows that if g_1 is a function of g, let us say $g_1 = f(g)$, this function is of the form $g_1 = kg$. *Thus, there are no inversely proportional magnitudes in the precise sense of the word "magnitude" that we have given.* Neither are there magnitudes that are dependent other than proportionally. Of course, two numbers can be connected in other ways than proportionally, but in such a case at least one of them is not a magnitude. If both are magnitudes, the relationship is reduced to proportionality. Now the family of magnitudes is vast. As we have seen, it includes numbers associated with geometry and physics and also numbers having to do with economic questions, such as the price of a piece of merchandise, the time necessary to manufacture it, etc.—hence the large number of proportionalities that we encounter.

Slightly doubtful or frankly inadmissible arguments will be replaced with correct reasoning by showing that one is dealing with magnitudes. To confine ourselves to purely mathematical concepts, let us make the following list of magnitudes: lengths of segments of a straight line, lengths of arcs of a curve, areas of plane domains, areas of portions of a surface, volumes of portions of space, measurements of angles, measurements of arcs of a circle, measurements of solid angles, measurements of portions of a sphere, time required for a moving body to cover the segments of its trajectory, variations in the speed from one end of such a segment to the other.

That these numbers are magnitudes is evident for the last two, and we have shown it for the first ones. The only ones that would require any verification (which I omit) are the measurements of solid angles and portions of a sphere, measurements that satisfy conditions (α), (β), and (γ).

Proportionalities between these magnitudes, when they exist, are easily proven. In the first place, it may happen that they are indicated by the following situation. When a moving body covers equal spaces in equal times, the distance covered and the time required are two proportional magnitudes associated with the arcs covered. Similarly, in the case of movement for which the velocity increases by equal amounts in equal times, the increase in velocity is proportional to the increase in time.

In other cases, it may happen that the operations performed in measuring one magnitude may be applicable step by step to some other magnitude (see section 21), for example, the proportionality of the measurements of arcs of circles to the central angles. This is also the case for measurements of portions of a sphere and measurements of the solid angles that cut these portions off.

92 *Application to Girard's theorem.*   We note also that every time one proves that a magnitude is completely determined (up to choice of unit) by conditions (α), (β), and (γ) for a certain family of bodies, one has shown that two magnitudes assigned to these bodies satisfying conditions (α), (β), and (γ) are proportional. We shall see shortly that it is advisable to state this truism, but let us first note the case in which the bodies depend only on a parameter of magnitude. In this case, as soon as we take a value g of a magnitude G assigned to a body, the magnitude of this body is determined. Thus, every other geometric magnitude G_1 assigned to it is determined. G and G_1 are proportional. This is the case, for example, for arcs of circles and central angles.

Let us consider a geometric magnitude g assigned to a polyhedral angle, say, the measure of that angle. Its value will not be sufficient to determine the magnitude of the angle; on the contrary, to that value there will correspond an infinite number of angles.

To this same angle, let us assign the number

$$h = \hat{A} + \hat{B} + \hat{C} + \cdots - (n - 2)\pi,$$

where n is the number of its dihedral angles and $\hat{A}$, $\hat{B}$, $\hat{C}$, ... are their measures in radians. Here each dihedral angle is measured inside the polyhedral angle.

If we decompose a polyhedral angle C into two other polyhedral angles, C_1 and C_2, we see immediately that we have $h = h_1 + h_2$ between the values of h for these three bodies. From this it follows that if we decompose C into trihedral angles, h will be the sum of the numbers assigned to these trihedral angles. For the case of one trihedral angle, h is positive, and hence, it is always positive. Therefore, it is a magnitude; furthermore, it is a geometric magnitude.

Now, the reasoning that I have omitted and that is analogous to part of the reasoning that led us to the concept of a plane area shows that a geometric magnitude assigned to a polyhedral angle is completely determined (up to choice of unit). Therefore, $g = kh$. With a suitable unit,

$$g = \hat{A} + \hat{B} + \hat{C} + \cdots - (n - 2)\pi.$$

This is Albert Girard's theorem (see section 74).

Legendre showed without using Euclid's axiom that the inequality

$$\pi - (\hat{A} + \hat{B} + \hat{C}) \geq 0$$

holds between the angles of a plane triangle, so that, for any plane polygon with n vertices,

$$h_1 = (n - 2)\pi - \hat{A} - \hat{B} - \hat{C} \cdots \geq 0.$$

It is obvious that h_1 either is a geometric magnitude assigned to plane polygons or it is zero. If, by reasoning in a manner different from what we have done, we had established the existence of the area of polygons without using Euclid's axiom (as is possible) and had shown that it was completely determined up to the unit, one might conclude further: either h_1 is proportional to the area when h_1 is not zero (this is the case of Lobachevskian geometry) or that h_1 is zero (this is the case of Euclidean geometry).

93 *Proportionality to several numbers. Critique.*   Now that we have brought out the theoretical as well as the practical interest in the concept of proportional magnitudes, I should replace what is ordinarily said with regard to magnitudes that are supposed proportional to other magnitudes with the following:

Suppose that a number g is determined by several other numbers x, y, z, and t and suppose that when one of these last numbers varies, g varies in proportion to it. Under these conditions,

$$g = Cxyzt,$$

where C is a constant.

To show this, suppose that g_0, x_0, y_0, z_0, t_0 constitute another system of associated numbers. We introduce the associated systems

$$g_1, x, y_0, z_0, t_0; \qquad g_2, x, y, z_0, t_0; \qquad g_3, x, y, z, t_0.$$

Then,

$$\frac{g_1}{g_0} = \frac{x}{x_0}, \qquad \frac{g_2}{g_1} = \frac{y}{y_0}, \qquad \frac{g_3}{g_2} = \frac{z}{z_0}, \qquad \frac{g}{g_3} = \frac{t}{t_0}$$

so that

$$g = xyzt \times \frac{g_0}{x_0 y_0 z_0 t_0}.$$

This proof assumes, however, that the auxiliary systems of values given to the set of variables do not leave the family F of those for which g is defined. This condition is not indispensable. It is *indispensable*, however, that we be able, without leaving F, to pass from x_0, y_0, z_0, t_0 to every x, y, z, t in F without varying more than one variable at any time and that there exist systems x, y, z, t for which the variables are all different from their initial values x_0, y_0, z_0, t_0. Thus, it is necessary that each variable be able to vary by itself, which excludes, for example, the case in which x is always equal to y and the case in which x and y are proportional magnitudes.

The preceding theorem is an elementary theorem in algebra. *It has nothing to do with magnitudes.* Let us start with a clear picture of the classic example of rectangular parallelepipeds. For the subfamily of rectangular parallelepipeds with two edges of given length, the length of the third is a magnitude proportional to the volume, so that we may apply the algebraic theorem above to the entire family of rectangular parallelepipeds with g representing the volume and x, y, z the lengths of the edges. But x, y, z are not magnitudes for this entire family (see section 90).

More generally, when we may apply the preceding theorem to numbers x, y, z, t, g, at least one of them is not a magnitude for the family of bodies with which we are dealing because *the only magnitudes g defined for a family of bodies F that are determined by magnitudes x, y, z, t relative to F are those that are proportional to one of the magnitudes x, y, z, or t.* Let us prove this, assuming, as above, that it is possible to pass from one body belonging to F to another by a succession of modifications, each of which varies only one of the magnitudes x, y, z, t and that condition

(c) is verified for the subfamilies of bodies obtained by these modifications. Then, in one such modification that varies only t, for example, either g is constant (that is, it does not depend on t) or g is proportional to t. If g depended on x, y, z, t, it would thus be of the form $Cxyzt$ by virtue of the preceding theorem. Now this is impossible since the equation

$$C(\xi + x)(\eta + y)(\zeta + z)(\tau + t) = C\xi\eta\zeta\tau + Cxyzt$$

does not hold for any system of positive numbers. Therefore, g does not depend on the four variables x, y, z, t. Similarly, it does not depend on any three of them or any two of them. This proves the proposition.

One cannot be too careful in the applications of these theorems. *In particular, one should make sure that the family A is sufficiently extensive that the condition regarding the passage from one body to another is actually verified.* Contrary to what one might be tempted to assume, it frequently happens that this is not the case, especially when the bodies constituting F depend on only a finite number of parameters. It is for this reason that the classical statement and proof of the supposed theorem on magnitudes proportional to several other magnitudes are inadmissible. In fact, if we were to apply the above theorems in such cases, we could arrive at quite paradoxical conclusions.

For instance, consider a material curve whose linear density increases constantly along the curve in a specified direction. The length l of an arc and its mass m are sufficient to determine it. Therefore, every other magnitude g assigned to this arc is determined by l and m. According to what was said above, it should be proportional to l or to m. Thus, the length of the projection of the arc onto a given plane and the quantity of heat necessary to increase the temperature of that arc by 1° would be declared proportional to the length or to the mass of the arc!

VII

INTEGRATION AND DIFFERENTIATION

94 *Magnitudes (body functions) and derived numbers (point functions).* The theory of magnitudes forming the subject of the preceding chapter was prepared by the researches of Cauchy on what he called concomitant magnitudes, by studies destined to clarify the concepts of area, volume, and measure, and also by studies made on linear functional operations. But it was in connection with the integration of the most general functions that numerous researchers collaborated in building a definitive theory. This should not be surprising since we have seen from the beginning that calculus and the theory of magnitudes had certain common goals. Furthermore, if we take the most general case, that is, the one in which we start with the fewest premises, we can now reason only about what is essential and fundamental to the question, and we have the possibility of clarifying our starting point. To have provided this elementary theory of magnitudes may turn out to be the most substantial result of the studies on the integration of discontinuous functions.

From the pedagogical point of view that we are now taking, the theory of magnitudes should have an effect on the presentation of the operations of integration and differentiation. The exposition that will be sketched below is made with an eye to students who hear for the first time of these functional operations in their general sense. Some previous sections (72, 75–77, 82) also dealt with teaching of the same students in the universities. We shall only point out the beginning of the exposition, dealing almost exclusively with the foundations. In actual teaching, one would need to be very careful with regard to form and, for example, one would not start with n-dimensional space.

Among the numbers considered by physicists, some, as we have seen, were assigned to points, and others to extended bodies, so that we have two mathematical concepts: functions of one or several variables and magnitudes. As long as they are physically determinable, these numbers have a certain continuity in that the same number is assigned to two practically indistinguishable points or bodies. We first need to translate these physical facts into purely logical statements.

Thus, we need to examine the use that physicists make of the numbers that they determine and, to do so, we must concentrate on what physicists call *a derived magnitude*.

Consider a body C. Physicists assign to it a mass M, a volume V, and a density (or average density) δ. The first two numbers are each determined experimentally, and the third results from them arithmetically by the defining formula

$$\delta = M/V.$$

To emphasize the distinction between these numbers, one says that the mass and the volume are directly measurable magnitudes and that the density is a derived magnitude. It will be noted that, in the preceding sentence, the word "magnitude" is used correctly (in the sense of the preceding chapter) when it is applied to the mass and to the volume but incorrectly when it is applied to the density. It is clear that if we partition two bodies into two sub-bodies, the density of the total body is not the sum of the densities of the two sub-bodies. Thus, we shall avoid this use of the word "magnitude."

For M and V to be determined, units of mass and volume must have been chosen, but there is no new choice to make for δ. This is what is meant when one says that the unit of density is a derived unit. A body will have a density equal to 1 and hence equal to unit density if, in particular, $M = 1$ and $V = 1$. This is the meaning of a statement like the following: When the unit of the mass is the gram and the unit of volume is the cubic centimeter, the unit of density will be the gram per cubic centimeter.

The average density of a body is particularly interesting when it is the same for all sub-bodies into which the body can be partitioned, that is, when this body is homogeneous with regard to mass. When this is not the case, physicists define a density at every point P of the body. It is the average density of bodies cut from the original body about P that are small enough to be practically homogeneous. We need to make mathematically precise the operation that yields this density. This operation is *differentiation*. The inverse operation, which enables us to calculate M by starting with V and δ, is *integration*.

To shorten matters, I shall start immediately with the case of a

k-dimensional space after reviewing the elements of k-dimensional geometry that we shall be needing.

95 *Review of k-dimensional geometry.*   On a curve, on a surface, or in ordinary space, a point is determined by one, two, or three coordinates. By analogy, we shall apply the word "point" in a k-dimensional space to a set of k numerical values arranged in a certain order, x_1, x_2, ... x_k, or, in abbreviated form, (x_i). The values of the x_i are called the coordinates. When we say that these coordinates are rectangular, we mean simply that the expression

$$\sqrt{\sum_i (x_i - x_i')^2}$$

will be called the distance between the two points (x_i) and (x_i'). We shall employ rectangular coordinates exclusively.

The formulae

$$X_i = \alpha_i + \sum_{j=1}^{j=k} a_i^j x_j$$

will be called the formulae for the transformation from the rectangular coordinates (x_i) to the rectangular coordinates (X_i) if the distance from (x_i) to (x_i') is always equal to the distance from (X_i) to (X_i'). An immediate calculation gives the conditions for orthogonality in the form

$$\sum_{i=1}^{i=k} (a_i^j)^2 = 1; \qquad \sum_{i=1}^{i=k} a_i^j a_i^k = 0, \qquad j \neq k.$$

It follows from this in classical fashion that the determinant Δ of the a_i^j is equal to ± 1. The formulae for change of coordinates solved for x_i and finally the orthogonality conditions in the second form also follow.

The formulae for change of coordinates can also be thought of as defining a point transformation. This transformation is said to be a displacement when $\Delta = 1$. Let us suppose that this is the case.

If $a_i^i = +1$ for every value of i, it follows from the orthogonality conditions that $a_i^j = 0$ for $i \neq j$. The displacement is then said to be a translation.

If $a_i^i = +1$, for one value of i, then $a_i^j = 0$ and $a_j^i = 0$ for that value of i, and if the α's are zeros, the displacement is called a rotation around the coordinate axis $x_1 = x_2 = \cdots = x_{i-1} = x_{i+1} = \cdots = x_k = 0$, known as the x_i-axis.

Two figures that correspond in a displacement are said to be equal.

It is immediately seen that one can pass from one figure to an equal figure by a translation and one or more rotations about the coordinate axes.

96 *Domains.* The inequalities

$$a_1 \leq x_1 \leq b_1,$$
$$a_2(x_1) \leq x_2 \leq b_2(x_1),$$
$$a_3(x_1, x_2) \leq x_3 \leq b_3(x_1, x_2),$$
$$a_k(x_1, x_2, \ldots, x_{k-1}) \leq x_k \leq b_k(x_1, x_2, \ldots, x_{k-1}),$$

in which the functions on the outside are continuous, define a family of points (x_i) constituting what is called *a simple domain.* If these functions are all constant (like a_1 and b_1), we have an *interval* whose k dimensions are the k differences $b_i - a_i$. By combination of a finite number of simple domains, we can get more general domains. However, the family of domains thus defined will depend on the coordinate axes and even on the order of these axes. To have a family of domains that is independent of the axes, let us agree that a set E of points will be called a domain if, for any $\epsilon > 0$, we can find a domain D_ϵ in the preceding sense of the word or a set D_ϵ of a finite number of domains such that the points of D_ϵ all belong to E and such that the points of E that do not belong to D_ϵ lie at a distance less than ϵ from points of D_ϵ and also such that D_ϵ contains $D_{\epsilon'}$ whenever ϵ is less than ϵ'.

I am not going into the easy proof of the invariance of this family of domains as one shifts from one system of axes to another. I wish simply to point out that for a logically complete exposition, such precision and proofs are indispensable even when we limit ourselves to not more than three dimensions.

97 *Quadrable domains.* In the preceding family of domains, we shall first isolate one particular family, namely, the family of plane domains with area such that

(α) *to each of these domains D is assigned a positive number $a_k(D)$;*

(β) *to a domain formed by the union of two other disjoint domains is assigned the sum of the two numbers assigned to those two domains;*

(γ) *equal numbers are assigned to two equal domains;*

(δ) *these numbers are completely fixed numerically when the number assigned to one of them is fixed.*

We shall say that these domains are quadrable of order k or, more briefly, that they are quadrable.

Also, we wish for this family to contain all the intervals and all the domains formed by combinations of a finite number of intervals.

Consider a complete grid T of intervals I, I_1, I_2, . . . , where the intervals I_p are defined by the inequalities

$$\frac{e_i}{10^p} \leq x_i \leq \frac{e_i + 1}{10^p},$$

the e_i being integers. For a given domain E, let us count the intervals I_p, all points of which belong to E. Suppose that there are n_p of them. Let us also count the intervals I_p that have some points belonging to E. Suppose that there are N_p of them.

Then, if the common area of order k of all the I is 1, the area of the I_p is necessarily $1/10^{kp}$ and that of E, if it exists, has a value between

$$n_p/10^{kp} \quad \text{and} \quad N_p/10^{kp}.$$

Also,

$$\frac{n_p}{10^{kp}} \leq \frac{n_{p+1}}{10^{k(p+1)}} \leq \frac{N_{p+1}}{10^{k(p+1)}} \leq \frac{N_p}{10^{kp}},$$

so that if $(N_p - n_p)/10^{kp}$ tends to zero as $1/p$ tends to zero, the area of order k of E can only be the common limit of the

$$n_p/10^{kp} \quad \text{and} \quad N_p/10^{kp}.$$

When this situation exists, E is said to be quadrable of order k and the limit is denoted by $a_k(E)$.

98 *The conditions of Chapter III.*   We have just gone back to the definition of Chapter III. We now need to show, as we did there for a_2, that a_k, which obviously satisfies conditions (α) and (δ), also satisfies (β) and (γ).

The intervals I that were counted in the N_p but not in the n_p are the ones that contain both points belonging to E and points not belonging to E. Thus, they are the intervals that contain boundary points. (A boundary point is any point (X_i) such that the interval $X_i - \epsilon \leq x_i \leq X_i + \epsilon$ contains, for any $\epsilon > 0$, points belonging to E and points not belonging to E.) As in section 27, from this follow both proposition (β) and the fact that a domain formed by the union of a finite number of other domains is quadrable of order k whenever the component domains are.

For proposition (γ), we proceed inductively by supposing it established for order $k - 1$. One could repeat word for word what was said in Chapter IV to pass from a_2 to a_3. One can also, the age of the audience allowing, present a less elementary argument that would pave the way for the operation of integration, as follows.

99 *Quadrature of simple domains.* We shall show that every simple domain in k-dimensional space is quadrable of order k by supposing the same property established for $k - 1$.

Suppose that E is the simple domain defined by the k double inequalities written above and that E' is the simple domain of $k - 1$ dimensions defined by the first $k - 1$ double inequalities. E' is said to be the projection of E onto the coordinate space $x_1, x_2, \ldots, x_{k-1}$.

The intervals I_p that we used above also have projections, which are the intervals I'_p of the grid T' by means of which we evaluate the areas of order $k - 1$ in the coordinate space in question. Thus, the I'_p provide for E' numbers n'_p and N'_p such that

$$a_{k-1}(E') - \frac{n'_p}{10^{(k-1)p}} \quad \text{and} \quad \frac{N'_p}{10^{(k-1)p}} - a_{k-1}(E')$$

tend to zero as p increases without bound.

The I_p provide numbers n_p and N_p for E. Let us consider all the I_p counted in the n_p or in the N_p. They constitute two domains $\underline{E}_p$ and $\overline{E}_p$. All those with the same projection I'_p belonging to $\underline{E}_p$ form an interval J_p, the first $k - 1$ dimensions of which are $1/10^p$ and the kth dimension differs from $b_k(x_1^0, x_2^0, \ldots x_{k-1}^0) - a_k(x_1^0, x_2^0, \ldots x_{k-1}^0)$, by at most η_p, where $x_1^0, x_2^0, \ldots, x_{k-1}^0$ is an arbitrarily chosen point belonging to that I'_p and the η_p tend to zero as p increases without bound. This I'_p is any one of the n'_p intervals used in order to have a value approaching $a_{k-1}(E')$ from below.

For such an interval I'_p, the intervals I_p of $\overline{E}_p$ whose projections are this I'_p yield an analogous result when the infinitesimal η_p is replaced by another ζ_p. But, in addition, $\overline{E}_p$ contains intervals I_p whose projections are the I'_p included in the N'_p but not in the n'_p. Those whose projections are the same I'_p also form an interval whose kth dimension is at most $M + \xi_p$, where M is the maximum of

$$b_k(x_1, x_2, \ldots, x_{k-1}) - a_k(x_1, x_2, \ldots, x_{k-1}).$$

Thus, we have

$$\frac{N_p - n_p}{10^{kp}} \le \Sigma \frac{1}{10^{(k-1)p}}(\eta_p + \varsigma_p) + \Sigma \frac{1}{10^{(k-1)p}}(M + \xi_p),$$

the two summations being over the two kinds of intervals I'_p that we have just been considering. Now this yields

$$\frac{N_p - n_p}{10^{kp}} \le a_{k-1}(E')(\eta_p + \varsigma_p) + (M + \varsigma_p)\frac{N'_p - n'_p}{10^{(k-1)p}}.$$

In this inequality, the second member tends to zero as p increases. This proves the theorem.

Furthermore, when b_k and a_k are constants (the case of a prismatic domain with generators parallel to the x_k-axis), the kth dimension of the J_p is constant up to $\eta_p + \varsigma_p$, and the sum of the $a_k(J_k)$ provides the value

$$a_k(E) = (b_k - a_k) \times a_{k-1}(E').$$

100   *Arbitrary quadrable domains.*   It also follows from this that such a prismatic domain has an area of order k, which does not change in any translation or in a rotation about the x_k-axis. We shall now extend this result to an arbitrary quadrable domain E of order k.

Let us form a figure $\underline{E}_p$ (or $\overline{E}_p$) with the aid of the intervals I_p, of which there are n_p (or N_p) and which provide a value approaching $a_k(E)$ from below (or from above). A translation or a rotation about the x_k-axis transforms these figures into figures equal to $\mathcal{E}$, $\underline{\mathcal{E}}_p$, and $\overline{\mathcal{E}}_p$ formed by the transformations of the I_p. These transformations are not in general intervals, but they are quadrable of order k and they always have an a_k equal to $1/10^{kp}$. Thus, $\underline{\mathcal{E}}_p$ and $\overline{\mathcal{E}}_p$ have the same values for a_k as do $\underline{E}_p$ and $\overline{E}_p$. Since $a_k(\overline{E}_p) - a_k(\underline{E}_p)$ tends to zero as p increases, the same is true for $a_k(\overline{\mathcal{E}}_p) - a_k(\underline{\mathcal{E}}_p)$. Therefore, $\mathcal{E}$ is quadrable; furthermore, its a_k is the limit of $a_k(\underline{\mathcal{E}}_p)$ and hence of $a_k(\underline{E}_p)$. Therefore $a_k(\mathcal{E}) = a_k(E)$.

The definition of area of order k is thus justified since one can always pass from one domain to an equal domain by a succession of displacements of the type described above.

In what follows, we shall deal exclusively with the family of quadrable domains, although this is not the only family that is interesting.

101   *Continuity.*   The definition of area of order k brought out the property of continuity that makes it possible for this area to be attained experimentally: To a domain E we have assigned two figures $\underline{E}_p$ and $\overline{E}_p$ made up of intervals I_p. To $\overline{E}_p$ we add all the I_{p+q} (with q fixed) that have points in $\overline{E}_p$ but are not contained in $\overline{E}_p$. If $\overline{E}_p$ were reduced to an I_p, the area of order k of these added I_{p+q} would be

$$\left[\frac{1}{10^p} + \frac{1}{10^{p+q}}\right]^k - \left(\frac{1}{10^p}\right)^k = a_k(I) \cdot \left\{\left(1 + \frac{1}{10^q}\right)^k - 1\right\}.$$

Thus, in the case of an arbitrary $\overline{E}_p$, these added I_{p+q} have an area of order k that is at most equal to

$$a_k(\overline{E}_p) \cdot \left\{\left(1 + \frac{1}{10^q}\right)^k - 1\right\}.$$

For sufficiently large q we will therefore have a figure $\overline{\overline{E}}_p$ such that $a_k(\overline{\overline{E}}_p)$ exceeds $a_k(\overline{E}_p)$ by as small an amount as we wish and hence, for p sufficiently large, it exceeds $a_k(E)$ by as small an amount as we wish if E is quadrable. Similarly, if we remove from $\underline{E}_p$ the I_{p+q} that are contained in $\underline{E}_p$ and that contain boundary points of $\underline{E}_p$, we will have a figure $\underline{\underline{E}}_p$ whose area of order k will, for sufficiently large p and q, be as close as we wish to $a_k(E)$.

Furthermore, all the I_{p+q} containing boundary points of E are contained in $\overline{\overline{E}}_p$ and none of them belongs to $\underline{\underline{E}}_p$.[1]

Let us now consider a variable quadrable domain E_v that tends to E. That is, whenever the conditions differ slightly enough from those under which we are seeking the limit, E_v is contained in an arbitrarily chosen domain containing E in its interior in the strict sense (and hence is contained in $\overline{\overline{E}}_p$) and contains a domain that is contained in E in the strict sense (and hence contains $\underline{\underline{E}}_p$). We then have

$$a_k(\underline{\underline{E}}_p) \leq a_k(E_v) \leq a_k(\overline{\overline{E}}_p).$$

Thus, *if the quadrable domain E is the limit of the quadrable domain E_v, then $a_k(E)$ is the limit of $a_k(E_v)$.*

102 *Functions of quadrable domains.* We shall now consider *domain functions.* The domains that will play the role of a variable are the quadrable domains. To each of these domains Δ let us suppose that a number $f(\Delta)$ is assigned; this is the domain function. In addition, let us

---

[1] The necessity for considering $\overline{\overline{E}}_p$ and $\underline{\underline{E}}_p$ follows from the facts that all the I_p containing boundary points of E do not necessarily belong to $\overline{E}_p$ (since E is not assumed to be closed in the set-theoretic sense) and that some of them may belong to $\underline{E}_p$.

assume that this function is *additive;* that is, it is such that, if we partition Δ into two quadrable domains Δ_1 and Δ_2, we have

$$f(\Delta) = f(\Delta_1) + f(\Delta_2).$$

Thus, the numbers $f(\Delta)$ satisfy condition (β). If, in addition, these numbers were positive, they would be magnitudes assigned to the bodies represented by the different quadrable domains. They are to magnitudes what the written numbers are to positive numbers. The amount of heat that one would have to supply to or extract from bodies in their actual state in order to give them a temperature of $0°$ is such an additive function.

We shall also assume that these functions are *continuous;* that is, if a variable Δ_v tends to Δ, the function $f(\Delta_v)$ will tend to $f(\Delta)$. This condition necessarily holds when $f(\Delta)$ can be determined experimentally.

A consequence of this continuity is the fact that $f(\Delta_v)$ tends to zero when Δ_v tends to zero in all its dimensions, that is, when Δ_v is contained in a variable interval whose largest dimension tends to zero. For, if this were not the case, one could choose Δ_v's whose dimensions tend to zero such that $f(\Delta_v)$ tends to a number $\varphi \neq 0$ and one could make the points of Δ_v have a limit point, let us say P, with coordinates (x_i^0). Then, in subdividing Δ_v if this is necessary, one may assume that, for every i, all its points verify either

$$x_i \leq x_i^0 \qquad \text{or} \qquad x_i \geq x_i^0,$$

all the while keeping the properties stated.

Let us suppose that, for each i, it is the *first* inequality that holds and that D is a domain for which P is a limit point and that all the points in D have coordinates greater than the coordinates of P. Then the limit of $D + \Delta_v$ would be D and $f(D + \Delta_v)$ would not tend to $f(D)$ but to $f(D) + \varphi$.

This property of the domain functions and of magnitudes that we are considering distinguishes them sharply from point functions. If we seek to reduce Δ to a point P, the value of $f(\Delta)$ tends to zero and not to a function of the point P like the density at P or the specific heat at P. We shall now obtain these point functions that correspond to the derived magnitudes of the physicists.

103 *Differentiation.*   Let us consider a function $f(\Delta)$ and a continuous magnitude $V(\Delta)$, that is, a continuous additive domain function that is also *positive.* The quotient $f(\Delta)/V(\Delta)$ has a meaning. We shall call it the mean derivative of f with respect to V in Δ. Let us decrease Δ in all its dimensions indefinitely but in such a way that it always contains a point P. If under these conditions the ratio tends to a definite limit $\varphi(P)$, *this limit will be the derivative of f with respect to V at P.* It is denoted by

$$\frac{df}{dV}(P) = \varphi(P).$$

The definition itself indicates the method of calculation that yields this derivative. The operation of differentiation is the calculation of the limit of a ratio. The most interesting case, and the only one that we shall examine, is the one in which the ratio tends uniformly to its limit, that is, the case in which the difference between $f(\Delta)/V(\Delta)$ and $\varphi(P)$ is less than an arbitrarily chosen positive number ϵ whenever Δ is contained in an interval whose k dimensions are at most equal to a number η, depending on ϵ but not on P, that tends to zero with ϵ.[1] Thus, if we choose for Δ the interval

$$x_i^0 - h \leq x_i \leq x_i^0 + h,$$

where P is the point (x_i^0), the ratio is a continuous function of P. Hence, its limit as k tends to zero will be a continuous function of P. Therefore, $\varphi(P)$ is continuous. We shall say that $\varphi(P)$ is a *derivative of uniform convergence*[2] when the incremential ratio $f(\Delta)/V(\Delta)$ tends uniformly to $\varphi(P)$.

When this is the case, this ratio is bounded whenever Δ is taken sufficiently small in all its dimensions, and, since on the other hand it is bounded for all the Δ's that are greater but are *taken in the bounded portion of space* that we are considering, the absolute value of $f(\Delta)/V(\Delta)$ is bounded for all the Δ's in question. We have

$$|f(\Delta)| < MV(\Delta),$$

where M is a fixed number. We say that the function f has bounded derivative with respect to V.

In particular, if the preceding inequality is true when we take $a_k(\Delta)$ for $V(\Delta)$, that is, if

$$|f(\Delta)| < Ka_k(\Delta)$$

for all Δ, the function $f(\Delta)$ is said to have a bounded derivative. It is

---

[1] Actually, except when $k = 1$, the uniform convergence of $f(\Delta)/V(\Delta)$ is a necessary consequence of the convergence of this ratio for every point P. This is true even for $k = 1$ if, under the same hypothesis, we use the general definition of domain at the end of section 96, which does not require connectedness.

[2] Actually, if a derivative is continuous it possesses uniform convergence.

clear that the physical examples of functions $f(\Delta)$ that have been given
have bounded derivatives. This obviously implies continuity of these
functions.

104   *Integration.*   Let us now state the problem of integration:
*Suppose that a continuous point function $\varphi(P)$ and a positive additive domain
function $V(\Delta)$ with bounded derivative are given. Find an additive function
$f(\Delta)$ with bounded derivative whose derivative of uniform convergence with
respect to V is $\varphi(P)$.*

If Δ is the union of a finite number of intervals δ_i and if we subdivide
these intervals where necessary, we may assume that their dimensions are
sufficiently small so that, for every i,

$$\left| \frac{f(\delta_i)}{V(\delta_i)} - \varphi(P_i) \right| < \epsilon,$$

where P_i is arbitrarily chosen in δ_i.

Then, since $f(\Delta) = \Sigma f(\delta_i)$, $\Sigma |V(\delta_i)| = \Sigma V(\delta_i) = V(\Delta)$, we have

$$|f(\Delta) - \Sigma \varphi(P_i)V(\delta_i)| < \epsilon V(\Delta).$$

Thus, if the solution $f(\Delta)$ exists, it is unique and equals the limit of
$\Sigma \varphi(P_i)V(\delta_i)$.

Let us see whether this limit exists. Consider another subdivision
of Δ. It will yield domains δ'_j and points P'_j. Let us suppose that the dimensions of the δ and the δ' are sufficiently small so that in each of these
intervals φ varies by an amount less than ϵ. Under this hypothesis, let
us evaluate the difference $\Sigma \varphi(P_i)V(\delta_i) - \Sigma \varphi(P'_j)V(\delta'_j)$.

Let δ'' be the intervals resulting from the inequalities defining the
δ_i's and the δ'_j's. Each δ_i and each δ'_j is a sum of δ'''s. Therefore, if
$\delta_i = \delta''_\alpha + \delta''_\beta + \cdots + \delta''_\lambda$, it follows that $V(\delta_i) = V(\delta''_\alpha) + V(\delta''_\beta) + \ldots +$
$V(\delta''_\lambda)$.

When this transformation for $V(\delta_i)$ and $V'(\delta_j)$ is made in the difference that we are evaluating, this difference takes the form of a summation
over the δ''''s:

$$\Sigma[\varphi(P_i) - \varphi(P'_j)]V(\delta''_\chi).$$

The $\varphi(P_i)$ and $\varphi(P'_j)$ thus associated with δ''_χ differ by at most ϵ from
the value assumed by φ at a point P_χ of δ''_χ. Therefore, the difference
that we are evaluating is at most $\Sigma 2\epsilon \times V(\delta''_\chi) = 2\epsilon V(\Delta)$.

Hence, it tends to zero with ϵ and *the sum $\Sigma \varphi(P_i)V(\delta_i)$ has a limit
$f(\Delta)$ that is independent of the method of subdivision of Δ.*

It remains to see if $f(\Delta)$ satisfies the conditions of the statement of the problem. In order to have to do this only once, let us first extend the results that we have obtained to an arbitrary quadrable domain Δ. We have seen that it is the limit of a variable domain Δ_v made up of intervals. Therefore, since we want $f(\Delta)$ to be continuous, $f(\Delta)$ must be the limit of $f(\Delta_v)$. And since $f(\Delta_v)$ is unique, it follows that $f(\Delta)$, if it exists, is unique. Let us show that $f(\Delta_v)$ does in fact have a limit. We have seen that it is possible to find two domains made up of intervals $\overline{\overline{\Delta}}$ and $\underline{\underline{\Delta}}$ such that Δ is strictly in the interior of the first and contains the second in the strict sense and such that $a_k(\overline{\overline{\Delta}} - \underline{\underline{\Delta}})$ is as small as we wish. Then, as Δ_v tends to Δ, it ends by being contained in $\overline{\overline{\Delta}}$ and containing $\underline{\underline{\Delta}}$. Let Δ_v and Δ_v' be two such domains. They have a common portion Δ'', they are such that $\Delta_v - \Delta'' = \Lambda$, $\Delta_v' - \Delta'' = \Lambda'$, where Λ and Λ' are contained in $\overline{\overline{\Delta}} - \underline{\underline{\Delta}}$, and they have areas of order k less than $a_k(\overline{\overline{\Delta}} - \underline{\underline{\Delta}})$. Let us evaluate

$$f(\Delta_v) - f(\Delta_v') = [f(\Delta'') + f(\Lambda)] - [f(\Delta'') + f(\Lambda')] = f(\Lambda) - f(\Lambda').$$

For Λ, which is made up of a finite number of intervals, $f(\Lambda)$ takes the form of a limit of a sum: $\Sigma\varphi(P_z)V(\delta_z)$. If B is the least upper bound of $|\varphi|$, the absolute value of this sum is at most

$$B\Sigma V(\delta_z) = BV(\Lambda) \le BKa_k(\Lambda),$$

where K is a fixed number. Therefore,

$$|f(\Delta_v) - f(\Delta_v')| \le 2BKa_k(\overline{\overline{\Delta}} - \underline{\underline{\Delta}}).$$

Hence, $f(\Delta_v)$ tends to a limit, which we can take for $f(\Delta)$.

105 *Law of the mean.*   This function $f(\Delta)$, the only one that can be a solution of our integration problem, can always be obtained as the limit of sums $\Sigma\varphi(P_i)V(\delta_i)$ taken over the intervals I_p (playing the role of the δ_i) counted in the n_p or the N_p, which provide approximating values of $a_k(\Delta)$.

From this follows a supremely important property of $f(\Delta)$, which will make it possible to show that $f(\Delta)$ does indeed satisfy all the conditions of the integration problem.

Theorem of the mean— If m and M are the greatest lower and least upper bounds of $\varphi(P)$ in Δ, then

$$f(\Delta) = \mu V(\Delta),$$

where μ lies between m and M.

To see this, let us calculate an approximate value of $f(\Delta)$ with the aid of n_p intervals I_p as stated. We get $\Sigma\varphi(P_i)V(\delta_i)$, which lies between $m\Sigma V(\delta_i)$ and $M\Sigma V(\delta_i)$, quantities which tend to $mV(\Delta)$ and $MV(\Delta)$. Since φ is a continuous function of P, the value of μ is one of the values taken by φ in Δ, from which we have another theorem:

Theorem of finite increments:

$$f(\Delta) = V(\Delta)\varphi(\pi),$$

where π is a point suitably chosen in the domain Δ.[1]

106　*Existence of the integral.*　　It follows from this theorem that if B is the least upper bound of $|\varphi|$ in the finite region of space that we are considering, and if for this region the function $V(\Delta)$, which has bounded derivative, is such that

$$V(\Delta) < K \cdot a_k(\Delta),$$

then

$$|f(\Delta)| < BK \cdot a_k(\Delta),$$

and $f(\Delta)$ *has a bounded derivative.*

If the domain Δ, which is quadrable of order k, is partitioned into two other quadrable domains Δ^1 and Δ^2, the n_p intervals I_p relative to Δ will be partitioned into the n_p^1 and n_p^2 relative to Δ^1 and Δ^2 and into remaining intervals R that contain points interior to Δ and boundary points of Δ^1 and Δ^2. Therefore, if we treat these I_p as δ_i, we get

$$\Sigma\varphi(P_i)V(\delta_i) = \Sigma^{\Delta^1}\varphi(P_i)V(\delta_i) + \Sigma^{\Delta^2}\varphi(P_i)V(\delta_i) + \Sigma^R\varphi(P_i)V(\delta_i).$$

As p increases without bound, the first three sums tend to $f(\Delta)$, $f(\Delta^1)$, $f(\Delta^2)$. The absolute value of the third is at most $BKa_k(R)$, which tends to zero. Therefore, $f(\Delta)$ *is an additive function.*[2]

The theorem of finite increments also yields

$$\frac{f(\Delta)}{V(\Delta)} - \varphi(P) = \varphi(\pi) - \varphi(P).$$

Therefore, the left-hand side of this equation is less than ϵ whenever the dimensions of Δ are taken sufficiently small so that φ varies by an amount less than ϵ between P and π, that is, between any two points of Δ.

---

[1] It is easily shown that $\mu = \varphi(\pi)$ is different from m and M except when $m = M$.

[2] This was evident for the Δ's that were sums of intervals, and we have already used it in that case.

Therefore, $f(\Delta)$ *admits $\varphi(P)$ as derivative with respect to V and this derivative is of uniform convergence.*

Thus, the possibility of solving the integration problem is proven. It is also proven that its solution is unique and is given by the limit of the sum $\Sigma\varphi(P_i)V(\delta_i)$ when the δ_i (disjoint and quadrable) have dimensions that tend to zero and make up a domain that approaches the given quadrable domain Δ and when the P_i are chosen arbitrarily in the δ_i with the same subscript. To recall this, we represent the solution (known as the definite integral, taken over Δ, of $\varphi(P)$ with respect to $V(\Delta)$) by the symbol

$$\int_\Delta \varphi(P)\, dV.$$

The additive function $f(\Delta)$ of the quadrable domain obtained by varying Δ is called the corresponding indefinite integral.

107 *Multiple integrals.*   The method of calculation that follows from the definition is rarely used in practice. Most frequently, we first replace integration with respect to $V(\delta)$ by integration with respect to $a_k(\delta)$. This is easy since it follows from

$$\frac{f(\delta)}{a_k(\delta)} = \frac{f(\delta)}{V(\delta)} \times \frac{V(\delta)}{a_k(\delta)}$$

that

$$\frac{df}{da_k}(P) = \frac{df}{dV}(P) \times \frac{dV}{da_k}(P) = \varphi(P) \cdot \frac{dV}{da_k}(P) = \psi(P).$$

This equation generalizes the theorem on the derivatives of functions of functions, and from it we get

$$\int_\Delta \varphi(P)\, dV = \int_\Delta \varphi(P) \cdot \frac{dV}{da_k}(P)\, da_k = \int_\Delta \psi(P)\, da_k.$$

An integral with respect to a_k is said to be a *multiple integral of order k.*

It is sufficient to learn to calculate these kth-order integrals. The calculation is made by iteration, at least for simple domains. We can confine ourselves to the latter case because, no matter what the quadrable domain E is, the domain that we have been calling $\bar{E}_p$ is infinitely close to it and is the sum of a finite number of simple domains in the form of the I_p (see section 101).

Let us study $\int_\Delta \varphi(P)\, da_k$, assuming that Δ is the simple domain defined by the inequalities of section 96 and that $\Delta(A, B)$ is obtained by replacing the first inequality defining Δ by

$$A \leq x_1 \leq B.$$

Suppose that $S(X_1)$ is the cross section of Δ made by $x_1 = X_1$, that is, the simple domain of the space $x_2, x_3, \ldots, x_k$ defined by the last $k - 1$ double inequalities when we take $x_1 = X_1$. This domain $S(X_1)$ varies continuously as X_1 varies.

Let us study the function $f[\Delta(A, B)]$ obtained by extending the integral to $\Delta(A, B)$. We can treat it as a function $F(\xi)$ of the one-dimensional interval ξ defined by

$$A \leq x_1 \leq B.$$

This function is clearly additive. Let us calculate its approximate value with the aid of the intervals I_p that have at least one point in $\Delta(A, B)$. The absolute value of this approximate value is bounded above by an expression of the form

$$\Sigma |\varphi(P_i)| a_k(\delta_i) \leq M a_k[\bar{\Delta}_p(A, B)],$$

where M is the least upper bound of $\varphi(P)$ and $\bar{\Delta}_p(A, B)$ is constructed as $\bar{E}_p$ was constructed above (see section 99). Now, all the I_p constituting $\bar{\Delta}_p(A, B)$ have a projection on the coordinate manifold $x_2, x_3, \ldots x_k$ formed by the I_p' of this manifold that have points belonging to the projection of Δ. Therefore, if A_{k-1} is the area of order $k - 1$ of this last projection, since the I_p that have the same projection I_p' form at most an interval J_p whose first dimension is at most $B - A + 2/10^p$, it follows that the least upper bound will exceed $M \cdot A_{k-1} \cdot (B - A)$ by as small an amount as we wish. Since $B - A$ is the area of order 1 of ξ, the absolute value of the incremental ratio of $F(\xi)$ is bounded above by $M \cdot A_{k-1}$. Thus, $F(\xi)$ has bounded derivative.

108 *The iterated integral.*   Let us make this calculation precise in order to obtain the derivative of $F(\xi)$ at the point $x_1 = A$.

To do this, we use intervals I' of sufficiently high subscript $p + q$ to construct the two domains $\underline{S}(A)$, $\overline{\overline{S}}(A)$, the first of which is properly contained in $S(A)$, which in turn is properly contained in the second (see section 101). Then, for B sufficiently close to A, $S(X_1)$ is, for X_1 varying from A to B, contained in $\overline{\overline{S}}(A)$ and contains $\underline{S}(A)$. Let us calculate an approximating value of $F(\xi)$ with the aid of the intervals I_{p+q+r}.

These intervals are of two kinds: some of them have projections I'_{p+q+r} on $x_2, x_3, \ldots x_k$ belonging to $\underline{S}(A)$; the projections of the others belong to $\overline{\overline{S}}(A) - \underline{S}(A)$. The value of a_{k-1} of the projections of the second kind of interval is at most equal to $a_{k-1}[\overline{\overline{S}}(A) - \underline{S}(A)]$, a quantity ϵ as small as we wish. By a calculation analogous to the preceding, these projections provide a contribution to the incremental ratio $F(\xi)/(B - A)$ that is at most equal in absolute value to $M\epsilon$, and hence arbitrarily small.

What is the contribution of the other intervals? In each of the I_{p+q+r} that have the same projection I'_{p+q+r}, let us choose a particular point such that these points have the same projection P' on $x_1 = A$. These I_{p+q+r} contribute to the incremental ratio a term of the form

$$\frac{1}{(B - A)} [\varphi(P_{i_1})a_k(\delta_{i_1}) + \varphi(P_{i_2})a_k(\delta_{i_2}) + \cdots + \varphi(P_{i_m})a_k(\delta_{i_m})].$$

Now the second term differs only very slightly from $\varphi(P')a_{k-1}(I'_{p+q+r})$ because the $\varphi(P_{i_j})$ differ from $\varphi(P')$ by an amount less than η whenever B is sufficiently close to A and, for sufficiently large r, the intervals δ_{i_j}, that is, the I_{p+q+r} with the same projection I'_{p+q+r}, form an interval whose first dimension differs as little as we wish from $|B - A|$.

Thus, to an arbitrarily close approximation, the incremental ratio will be

$$\Sigma\varphi(P'_i)a_{k-1}(\delta'_i).$$

The derivative will exist if this quantity has a limit under the conditions assumed. Now this limit is known and is equal to

$$\int_{s(A)} \varphi(P)\,da_{k-1},$$

hence $F(\xi)$ has a derivative

$$\frac{dF}{da_1} = \int_{s(A)} \varphi(P)\,da_{k-1}.$$

The convergence of the incremental ratio to the derivative, which is its limit, is uniform, and, consequently,

$$F(\xi) = \int_{\xi} \left[\int_{s(A)} \varphi(P)\,da_{k-1}\right] da_1.$$

The calculation of the kth-order integral is replaced by calculation of the simple integral of a $(k - 1)$st-order integral.

A simple integral is denoted by

$$\int_{\xi} \chi(P)\,da_1 = \int_A^B \chi(x_1)\,dx_1,$$

if $A < B$, in order to emphasize that the measure (or area of order 1) of an interval ($A \leq x_1 \leq B$) is the increment that we give the variable x_1 and that the value of x_1 determines P.

Thus, in the particular case in which $A = a_1$ and $B = b_1$, the formula obtained becomes

$$f(\Delta) = \int_a^{b_1} \left[\int\int_{S(x_1)} \varphi(P) \, da_{k-1} \right] dx_1.$$

Then, by induction,

$$f(\Delta) = \int_{a_1}^{b_1} \left\{ \int_{a_2(x_1)}^{b_2(x_1)} \left[\cdots \left(\int_{a_k(x_1, x_2, \ldots, x_{k-1})}^{b_k(x_1, x_2, \ldots, x_{k-1})} \varphi(P) \, dx_k \right) \cdots \right] dx_2 \right\} dx_1.$$

If we group the first n integral signs on the one hand, and the last $k - n$ integral signs on the other, we have a formula that could easily be proven directly:

$$f(\Delta) = \int_{P_{1,2,\ldots,n}} \left[\int\int_{S(x_1, x_2, \ldots, x_n)} \varphi(P) \, da_{k-n} \right] da_n.$$

$P_{1,2,\ldots,n}$ is the projection of Δ onto the coordinate space $x_1, x_2, \ldots,$ x_n. $S(x_1, x_2, \ldots, x_n)$ is the section of Δ made by the space parallel to the coordinate space indicated and passing through the point P. That is, the first n double inequalities that define Δ also define $P_{1,2,\ldots,n}$, and the $k - n$ (when we fix $x_1, x_2, \ldots, x_n$) define $S(x_1, x_2, \ldots, x_n)$.

These formulae make it possible to evaluate multiple integrals by integrations of lower order and, in general, to use inductive reasoning. In particular, if we set $\varphi(P) \equiv 1$, we have formulae connecting the area of order k with areas of lower orders. From this we get, in particular, the calculations of areas (in the ordinary sense of the word) and volumes.

109 *Antiderivatives.* Thus, all that remains is to learn how to carry out simple integrations. Let us define

$$F(\xi) = \int_{A \leq x \leq B} \varphi(x) \, dx,$$

which is also a function of two variables $\Phi(A, B)$. It follows from the fact that F is additive, that for $A < B < C$,

$$\Phi(A, B) + \Phi(B, C) = \Phi(A, C).$$

Therefore, for $0 < A < B$,

$$F(\xi) = \Phi(0, B) - \Phi(0, A).$$

For this formula to remain valid for $A < B < 0$ and for $A < 0 < B$, we need only set $\Phi(X, Y) = -\Phi(Y, X)$. This convention is legitimate since Φ has not been defined previously except when we assumed the value of the first variable to be smaller than the value of the second. Thus we have

$$\int_A^B \varphi(x)\, dx = \Phi(0, B) - \Phi(0, A),$$

whatever the signs of A and B may be, provided only that A is less than B. We finally remove this last restriction when we set (by definition)

$$\int_A^B \varphi(x)\, dx + \int_B^A \varphi(x)\, dx = 0.$$

Thus, $F(\xi)$ depends only on one function of one variable $\Phi(0, X) = \Psi(X)$, even when (as we have just done) we define $F(\xi)$ for negative intervals $[A > B]$. What property of Ψ corresponds to the differentiability of F?

For $A < B$, we have

$$\frac{F(\xi)}{a_1(\xi)} = \varphi(X) \quad \text{with } A < X < B$$

because of our theorem on finite increments, and we have

$$\frac{F(\xi)}{a_1(\xi)} = \frac{\Psi(B) - \Psi(A)}{B - A}$$

from what was said above. Therefore,

$$\frac{\Psi(B) - \Psi(A)}{B - A} = \varphi(X).$$

$\Psi(X)$ admits $\varphi(X)$ as its derivative and, what is more, we see that the incremential ratio of Ψ tends uniformly to the derivative.[1]

Thus, any continuous function $\varphi(X)$ of a single variable has antiderivatives. Furthermore, they are determined up to a constant in accordance with the classical derivation. Hence, if we know one of these antiderivatives $\Psi_0(X)$, we deduce

$$\Phi(0, X) = \Psi_0(X) + c = \Psi_0(X) - \Psi_0(0),$$

so that

$$\int_A^B \varphi(x)\, dx = \Psi_0(B) - \Psi_0(A).$$

Thus, the calculation of multiple integrals is reduced to calculation of antiderivatives of functions of one variable.

It should also be remarked that in the case of a single dimension,

---

[1] I am assuming that the concepts of a derivative and of a primitive function of functions of one variable are known. These concepts are included in teaching programs at the secondary level.

an additive domain function (hence a function of *one-dimensional in-tervals*) is, from what was said above, determined when we know its continuous derivative; it is not necessary that we know in advance that the desired function has a bounded derivative or that the derivative possesses uniform convergence. This function is the indefinite integral of the derivative. This remark, of slight importance in itself, is indispensable to the rigor of the exposition adopted here.

110 *Change of variable in integration.*   We shall rapidly justify the formula given for change of variables in integral calculus. Naturally, we assume that the theory of implicit functions and everything concerning the change of variables in differential calculus is known.

This change of variables puts a point (u_i) in correspondence with a point (x_i) and puts a domain δ_x of the space of the x_i in correspondence with a domain δ_u of the space of the u_i. If it is established that to every quadrable δ_x of order k there corresponds a quadrable δ_u and conversely, and if it is established that the ratios $a_k(\delta_x)/a_k(\delta_u)$ and $a_k(\delta_u)/a_k(\delta_x)$ remain less than some number M, then a function $f(\delta_x)$ that is additive and with bounded derivative may be considered as a function of δ_u that is additive and of bounded derivative since

$$\frac{f(\delta_x)}{a_k(\delta_u)} = \frac{f(\delta_x)}{a_k(\delta_x)} \times \frac{a_k(\delta_x)}{a_k(\delta_u)}.$$

If

$$f(\delta_x) = \int_{\delta_x} \varphi(P)d[a_k(\delta_x)],$$

the first ratio in the right member tends uniformly to

$$\frac{d[f(\delta_x)]}{d[a_k(\delta_x)]}(P) = \varphi(P).$$

Therefore, if it is established that the second ratio tends uniformly to a limit

$$\frac{d[a_k(\delta_x)]}{d[a_k(\delta_u)]}(P) = \chi(P),$$

the ratio of the first member must tend uniformly to a limit, and we have

$$f(\delta_x) = \int_{\delta_u} \varphi(P)\cdot\chi(P)d[a_k(\delta_u)].$$

This formula solves the problem of change of variable. More generally, it can be applied to change the function with respect to which one is integrating:

$$f(\Delta) = \int_\Delta \varphi(P)\, dV = \int_\Delta \varphi(P) \cdot \frac{dV}{dV_1}\,(P) \cdot dV_1.$$

We have already encountered this interpretation in section 107.

As a formula for change of variable, this formula assumes that we justified our assumptions. Let us first examine the hypothesis $k = 1$.

The formula for change of variable is $x = A(u)$, where $A'(u)$ is of constant sign. To any interval there corresponds an interval, and, since we are treating only intervals as domains δ_x, there is no question of the quadrability of order 1 of the domains δ_u.

If δ_x is (x_1, x_2) and if δ_u is (u', u''), we have

$$\frac{\delta[a_k(\delta_x)]}{\delta[a_k(\delta_u)]} = \left|\frac{x^1 - x^2}{u' - u''}\right| = \left|\frac{A(u') - A(u'')}{u' - u''}\right|.$$

Thus, the incremental ratio is uniformly bounded, as is its reciprocal. Furthermore, we see that it tends uniformly to a limit $|A'(u)|$.

Thus, we have

$$\int_{\Delta_x} \varphi(x)\, dx = \int_{\Delta_u} \varphi[A(u)] \cdot |A'(u)|\, du.$$

We note that the *absolute-value* sign is needed only when $A'(u)$ is negative, that is, with $x_1 = A(u'')$ and $x_2 = A(u')$, if the transformation makes the negative orientation of the u-axis correspond to the positive orientation of the x-axis, that is, the transformation changes the orientation.

Suppose now that $k > 1$. Let only x_k be changed by the formula

$$x_k = A[x_1, x_2, \ldots, x_{k-1}, u_k],$$

in which $\partial A/\partial u_k$ is of constant sign. Let

$$u_k = B[x_1, x_2, \ldots, x_{k-1}, x_k]$$

be the inverse function.

Corresponding to the domain Δ_x defined by the inequalities of section 96 is the domain Δ_u defined by the first $k - 1$ inequalities and by u_k, which is between $B[x_1, x_2, \ldots, x_{k-1}, a_k(x_1, x_2, \ldots, x_{k-1})]$ and $B[x_1, x_2, \ldots, x_{k-1}, b_k(x_1, x_2, \ldots, x_{k-1})]$. The second of these values of B will be greater than the first if and only if A'_{u_k} is positive. Let us call the smaller value α_k and the larger value β_k. Then, if we denote by D the common projection Δ_x and Δ_u onto the coordinate manifold $x_1, x_2, \ldots x_{k-1}$ and by d any portion of D, we have

$$\int_{\Delta_x} \varphi(P) d[a_k(\delta_x)] = \int_D \left[\int_{a_k(x_1,x_2,\,\ldots\,,x_{k-1})}^{b_k(x_1,x_2,\,\ldots\,,x_{k-1})} \varphi(P)\, dx_k \right] d[a_{k-1}(d)].$$

From the preceding formula, this is equal to

$$\int_D \left[\int_{\alpha_k(x_1,x_2,\,\ldots\,,x_{k-1})}^{\beta_k(x_1,x_2,\,\ldots\,,x_{k-1})} \varphi(P) \cdot \left| \frac{\partial A(x_1, x_2, \ldots, x_k)}{\partial u_k} \right| \cdot du_k \right] d[a_{k-1}(d)]$$

$$= \int_{\Delta_u} \varphi(P) \left| \frac{\partial A}{\partial u_k} \right| (P)\, d[a_k(\delta_u)].$$

This has been established only for a simple domain relative to the order x_1, x_2, ... x_k of the variables. However, since every quadrable domain Δ_x differs by as small an amount as we wish from a sum of intervals, and hence from a sum of simple domains, the formula holds in general.

We note again that the *absolute-value* sign is necessary only if the positive directions of the u- and x-axes do not correspond. When this is not the case and $k = 1, 2,$ or 3, we say that there is a change of orientation, and hence we shall employ the same expression in the general case.

Suppose now that we let

$$x_i = A_i(u_1, u_2, \ldots, u_k), \qquad (i = 1, 2, \ldots, k),$$

with the classical conditions (which I do not state) satisfied. The classical proof of the implicit-function theorem shows that the *bounded* region in which we are studying the transformation can be partitioned into a finite number of subregions such that in each of them we may make the change of variable by making k changes of a single variable.[1]

By partitioning the original domain as necessary, we may assume that we have a domain situated entirely in one of these regions. Let us suppose that it is the one where we pass successively from x_1 to u_1, from x_2 to u_2, ... , from x_k to u_k. The formulae will then be of the form

$$x_i = B_i(u_1, u_2, \ldots, u_i, x_{i+1}, \ldots, x_k)$$

or

$$u_i = C_i(u_1, u_2, \ldots, u_{i-1}, x_i, \ldots, x_k).$$

---

[1] To prove the implicit-function theorem, one shows that, in a neighborhood of every point, it is possible, by permuting the subscripts in the two series of variables if necessary, to arrange for the minors obtained by eliminating the first line and column of the determinant of the $\partial A_i/\partial u_i$ to be all different from zero. Hence, this is true for an entire region around each point. These are the subregions referred to in the text.

With regard to the fact that they are finite in number, which is clear from the so-called Borel-Lebesgue theorem,* it can easily be proven in a more elementary manner if we assume, for example, the existence of second derivatives of the A_i.

  * Every open covering of a complete compact n space includes a finite covering. (Ed.)

The k successive factors that these k changes introduce into the integral that is being transformed are the partial derivatives

$$\left|\frac{\partial B_i}{\partial u_i}\right| = \frac{1}{|\partial C_i/\partial x_i|}.$$

Now C_i is obtained by solving the last $k - i + 1$ equations $x_i = A_i$ for $u_i, u_{i+1}, \ldots, u_k$. Therefore,

$$\frac{\partial C_i}{\partial x_i} = \frac{\dfrac{D(A_{i+1}, \ldots, A_k)}{D(u_{i+1}, \ldots, u_k)}}{\dfrac{D(A_i, \ldots, A_k)}{D(u_i, \ldots, u_k)}} (P).$$

Consequently, we have

$$\int_{\Delta_x} \varphi(P) d[a_k(\delta_x)] = \int_{\Delta_u} \varphi(P) \cdot \left|\frac{D(A_1, \ldots, A_k)}{D(u_1, \ldots, u_k)} (P)\right| \cdot d[a_k(\delta_u)].$$

This is the desired formula. Δ_x and Δ_u are two domains that correspond by the given formulae.

111 *Orientation of domains.*   Let us pause an instant to explain carefully that last sentence, because in the question propounded there are actually no corresponding domains. Therefore, let us make more precise the beginning of section 110.

We started with an integral over domains forming part of a curve or surface or, more generally, of what is called a manifold:

$$X_j = X_j(x_1, x_2, \ldots, x_k),$$

where j varies from 1 to m, with $m \geq k$.

The X_j are coordinates, rectangular coordinates for example, which are called rectilinear to distinguish them from the parameters x_i, which are also called curvilinear coordinates of the manifold. The preceding manifold is said to be a k-dimensional manifold embedded in m-dimensional space.

Consider a point P of that manifold. By hypothesis, it is given by one and only one system of values x_i. Therefore, if we interpret these x_i as rectilinear, or more precisely, rectangular coordinates in the k-dimensional space of the x_i, we have a point P_x that is the image of P. Thus, to a domain D of the manifold there corresponds a domain D_x of the space of the x_i.

Let us now make a change of curvilinear coordinates with the aid of the formulae $x_i = A_i(u_1, u_2, \ldots, u_k)$. The X_j are expressed as functions of the u_i, so that we have a new image of P, namely, the point P_u in the space of the u_i. The passage from P_x to P_u is defined by the intermediary passage P_x to P and then P to P_u. There is a correspondence between P_x and P_u, and the formulae given above are also the formulae for a transformation from the space of the x_i into the space of the u_i; hence, between corresponding domains.

All this is very banal and completely analogous to what we saw in the case in which the A_i were linear: the formulae for change of coordinates are also the formulae for a point transformation. In this particular case, the transformation was said (when it is a matter of rectangular coordinates) to be a displacement when the determinant of the transformation was positive. When this determinant is negative, we speak of a *transformation by symmetry* since a change of sign of only one coordinate is sufficient to have a symmetry and, consequently, the meaning of this phraseology agrees completely with the wording used above in the case of $k \leq 3$.

Among these transformations of rectilinear coordinates, there are two very simple ones: change of sign of one coordinate and permutation of the order of two coordinates. For spaces of 1, 2, or 3 dimensions, we usually say that we change from one orientation to another. We shall keep this terminology in the general case.

Thus, choosing a system of curvilinear coordinates of a manifold implies choice of an orientation on that manifold. When a change of curvilinear coordinates is made, the orientation is or is not changed, depending on whether the functional determinant of the original coordinates with respect to the new ones is negative or positive.

Now that this is said, a function defined for the domains D can equally well be considered as assigned to the domain D_x or D_u. Thus, in the preceding section, to every domain δ there were assigned successively the functions $a_k(\delta_x)$ and $a_k(\delta_u)$. An integral $\int_\Delta \varphi(P) \, dV$ does not change its notation when we make a change of curvilinear coordinates. However, if we wish to remind anyone that we may use either the coordinates x_i or the coordinates x_u, we may write

$$\int_{\Delta_x} \varphi(P_x) d[V(\delta_x)] = \int_{\Delta_u} \varphi(P_u) d[V(\delta_u)].$$

And this brings out clearly the fact that the formulae for the transformation of a calculation made with the x_i into a calculation made with the u_i, that is, the formulae for change of variable, will also be formulae for the transformation of the domain Δ_x of the space of the x_i into a domain Δ_u of the space of the u_i. In each of these spaces, one orientation has been chosen as the positive orientation. Unless the contrary is stated, it is the orientation determined by the order of the subscripts of the coordinates.

112 *A new definition of an integral.* Thus, it follows from what was said above that

$$\int_{\Delta_x} \varphi(P)d[a_k(\delta_x)] = \int_{\Delta_u} \varphi(P) \cdot \frac{D(A_1, \ldots, A_k)}{D(u_1, \ldots, u_k)} (P) \cdot d[a_k(\delta_u)]$$

if the formulae, when considered as defining a change of curvilinear coordinates, conserve the orientation or if, when they are considered as formulae for a transformation, they make the positive orientations of the spaces x_i and u_i correspond.

Otherwise, we have

$$\int_{\Delta_x} \varphi(P)d[a_k(\delta_x)] = \int_{\Delta_u} \varphi(P) \cdot (-1) \cdot \frac{D(A_1, \ldots, A_k)}{D(u_1, \ldots, u_k)} (P)d[a_k(\delta_u)].$$

These two formulae can be combined into a single one if we distinguish the domains not only by family of their points but also by the orientation assigned to them. Thus, to a single unoriented domain Δ correspond two oriented domains $\underset{\to+}{\Delta}$, $\underset{\to-}{\Delta}$ with positive and negative orientation. Then, for any change of curvilinear coordinates or any transformation, we have

$$\int_{\underset{\to}{\Delta_x}} \varphi(P)d[a_k(\delta_x)] = \int_{\underset{\to}{\Delta_u}} \varphi(P) \frac{D(A_1, \ldots, A_k)}{D(u_1, \ldots, u_k)} (P)d[a_k(\delta_u)]$$

(where the two oriented domains $\underset{\to}{\Delta_x}$, $\underset{\to}{\Delta_u}$ are those that correspond to each other), provided we set

$$\int_{\underset{\to+}{\Delta}} \varphi(P)\, dV = \int_{\Delta} \varphi(P)\, dV,$$

and

$$\int_{\underset{\to+}{\Delta}} \varphi(P) \cdot dV + \int_{\underset{\to-}{\Delta}} \varphi(P) \cdot dV = 0.$$

This convention is the one made in section 109 for the case of a single coordinate. Other conventions are tied up with this one almost automatically. The two integrals in the above equation are the limits of the sums

$$\Sigma\varphi(P_i)V(\delta_i), \qquad -\Sigma\varphi(P_i)V(\delta_i) = \Sigma\varphi(P_i)[-V(\delta_i)].$$

The δ_i result from the partitioning of Δ. However, in the first case, it has to do with $\Delta_{\to+}$ and in the second with $\Delta_{\to-}$. Therefore, it is natural to write these two sums in the same form

$$\Sigma\varphi(P_i)V(\delta_i),$$

where the orientation of the δ_i is the same as the orientation of Δ. This amounts to setting

$$V(\delta_i)_{\to+} = V(\delta_i); \qquad V(\delta_i)_{\to+} + V(\delta_i)_{\to-} = 0.$$

From this, we get a new convention: *when an additive function $V(\delta)$ is given for unoriented domains, a function defined by the above equations for oriented domains is derived from it.*

At the same time, it turns out that we have defined the integral of $\varphi(P)$ with respect to a domain function that is always negative, namely, the function $-V$. The only reason for our assuming that $V > 0$ in section 103 and the following sections was to ensure that the incremental ratio $f(\Delta)/V(\Delta)$ exists. This would have been guaranteed just as well if we had assumed V to be always negative. In the theory that we have given, we would only have needed to change certain words and the direction of a few inequalities and to insert a few absolute-value symbols. It is not worthwhile to take up these things again in detail. It is sufficient to agree that, by definition, we always have

$$\int \varphi(P)\,dV + \int \varphi(P)d[-V] = 0$$

whether Δ is an oriented or an unoriented domain.

In contrast, if $V(\Delta)$ had been able to take both signs, we would have had to bring in some serious modifications because, for certain Δ's, the incremental ratio with respect to V would not have existed. However, let us suppose that the region in question may be partitioned into a finite number of regions such that, for the domains contained in one of these regions, V has a constant sign. Then, if we partition every domain Δ into subdomains $\Delta', \Delta'', \ldots$, lying in these different regions, we set

$$\int_\Delta = \int_{\Delta'} + \int_{\Delta''} + \cdots.$$

The integral defined in this way will enjoy almost all the properties that we have mentioned. However, the theorem on finite increments and the theorem of the mean should be applied only to the subdomains, and we can no longer obtain the indefinite integral at the boundary points of the subregions. In any case, *the integral is now defined with respect to an additive domain function that is not always positive and that is extended to an oriented domain.*

113 *Transformation of oriented integrals.* Suppose that

$$x_i = F_i(u_1, u_2, \ldots, u_k),$$

where the formulae ($i = 1, 2, \ldots, n$) define a k-dimensional manifold in n-dimensional space. Since we wish for only one system of numbers u_i to correspond to any one point of this manifold and since we wish for this to be assured by the ordinary theorem on implicit functions, we assume, apart from the existence and continuity of the numbers $\partial F_i / \partial u_j$, that the minors with k rows and k columns of the matrix of these derivatives do not all vanish simultaneously. Then the closed region in question is, under these conditions, the sum of a finite number of regions for each of which k coordinates suitably chosen from among the n rectilinear coordinates x_i can serve as curvilinear coordinates for the manifold. If they are the variables

$$x_1, x_2, \ldots, x_k,$$

we have

$$u_i = A_i(x_1, x_2, \ldots, x_k)$$

for $i \le k$, and, for $p > k$,

$$x_p = G_p(x_1, x_2, \ldots, x_k).$$

We shall have a correspondence between the domains Δ of the manifold, the domains Δ_u of the space of the u_i, and (if Δ is in the given region R of the manifold), the domains Δ_x of the space $x_1, x_2, \ldots, x_k$. Furthermore, there is a correspondence between the orientations of these domains. If, as we have supposed, the positive orientation of Δ corresponds to the positive orientation of Δ_u, we shall have in Δ_x a positive or a negative orientation, depending on whether the determinant

$$\frac{D(x_1, \ldots, x_k)}{D(u_1, \ldots, u_k)}$$

is positive or negative.

Let us now turn from the region R to a region R_1. With the orientation on the manifold chosen once and for all, the orientation of the Δ

and of the Δ_u will not vary, but the orientation of the Δ_x will vary if the functional determinant has different signs in R and R_1. Thus, if the functional determinant in question

$$\frac{D(x_1, x_2, \ldots, x_k)}{D(u_1, u_2, \ldots, u_k)}$$

does not change sign except at exceptional points, which do not constitute a region of the manifold and consequently can be omitted in the calculation of the integral $\int_D \varphi(P)d[a_k(\delta_u)]$ for every domain D,[1] we have

$$\int_{\underset{\rightarrow}{D}} \varphi(P)d[a_k(\delta_u)] = \int_{\underset{\rightarrow}{D}} \varphi(P)\frac{D(u_1, u_2, \ldots, u_k)}{D(x_1, x_2, \ldots, x_k)}(P)d[a_k(\delta_x)],$$

where the symbol $\underset{\rightarrow}{D}$ indicates that in the expression on the right we should assign to every domain δ of the manifold situated in one of the regions $R, R_1, \ldots$ the area of order k of its projection δ_x and that we should assign to this area the sign corresponding to the orientation of δ_x as the projection of the part $\underset{\rightarrow}{\delta}$ of the oriented domain $\underset{\rightarrow}{D}$.

The formula obtained above can be written

$$\int_{\underset{\rightarrow}{D}} \psi(x_1, x_2, \ldots, x_u)d[a_k(\delta_x)] = \int_{\underset{\rightarrow}{D}} \psi(P) \cdot \frac{D(x, \ldots, x_k)}{D(u_1, \ldots, u_k)}(P)d[a_k(\delta_u)].$$

It defines the symbol on the left-hand side, which is a line integral if $k = 1$ and is a surface integral if $k = 2$.

In the event that the manifold containing D is exceptional and contains regions at all the points of which the determinant in the right-hand member is zero, these regions would be considered as making no contribution to the value of the integral.

The case in which the variables x_i that are used are not the first k variables as arranged in the natural order of their subscripts is immediately reduced to the preceding case since changing the order of two variables changes only the sense of the orientations and hence the signs of the a_k.

114　Green's theorem.

114 *Green's theorem.*　　An important application of this definition is Green's theorem and its generalizations.

Let us look again at the last formula in section 108 for the case of

---

[1] This holds except for very exceptional manifolds, specifically, in the case of three dimensions except for curves that contain arcs in the planes $x_i = $ const and except for surfaces containing portions of cylinders with generators parallel to $x_k = x_i = 0$.

the simple domain defined by the inequalities of section 96. It is written

$$\int_\Delta \varphi(P)\, dA_k = \int_{P_{1,2,\ldots,k-1}} \left[\int_{a_k(x_1,x_2,\ldots,x_{k-1})}^{b_k(x_1,x_2,\ldots,x_{k-1})} \varphi(x_1, x_2, \ldots, x_k)\, dx_k \right] dA_{k-1},$$

where the symbols A_k and A_{k-1} represent areas of order k and $k-1$.

If

$$\varphi(x_1, x_2, \ldots, x_k) = \frac{\partial}{\partial x_k} F(x_1, \ldots, x_k)$$

in the right member of the preceding formula, we can perform a simple integration:

$$\int_{P_{1,\ldots,k}} F[x_1, \ldots, x_{k-1}, b_k(x_1, \ldots, x_{k-1})]\, dA_{k-1}$$

$$- \int_{P_{1,\ldots,k}} F[x_1, x_2, \ldots, x_{k-1}, a_k(x_1, \ldots, x_k)]\, dA_{k-1}.$$

Suppose also that the two boundary manifolds of Δ

$$x_k = a_k(x_1, \ldots, x_{k-1}),$$
$$x_k = b_k(x_1, \ldots, x_{k-1}),$$

are two portions Σ_1 and Σ_2 of a $(k-1)$-dimensional manifold $x_i = S_i(u_1, \ldots, u_{k-1})$, possessing all the regularity characteristics mentioned above.

The functional determinant $\dfrac{D(S_1, S_2, \ldots, S_{k-1})}{D(u_1, u_2, \ldots, u_{k-1})}$ has a constant sign in Σ_1 and in Σ_2 since $x_1, \ldots, x_{k-1}$ may be substituted in it for $u_1, \ldots, u_{k-1}$. This determinant changes its sign, on the other hand, in every region containing a common boundary point of Σ_1 and Σ_2 since substitution of the type just mentioned is impossible in such a case.[1]

Now this functional determinant is the one that fixes the orientation to be given to a domain projected onto the coordinate space $x_1, \ldots, x_{k-1}$ when an orientation of the manifold has been chosen. Therefore, if we take on Σ the orientation that projects Σ_2 with a positive orientation, the value of the integral will be

$$\int_{\underset{\rightarrow}{\Sigma}} F[P] \cdot d[A_{k-1}(\underline{\delta_{x_1}, \ldots, x_{k-1}})].$$

This result constitutes Green's formula. It can be completed in the usual way by examining other domains and also in the case in which the

---

[1] This assertion needs to be made more precise. It rests on a more general form of the implicit-function theorem than the classical statement, which assumes finite and *nonzero* functional determinants. If we confine ourselves to ordinary space and to the plane, it will be easy to make the above assertion more precise, and we shall thus have the necessary directions for treating the general case.

variables that are kept are not the coordinates $x_1, x_2, \ldots, x_{k-1}$ arranged in the natural order of the subscripts.

115 *Generalization of length and area.*   Another important application of the principle of change of variable is the generalization of the concept of length of a curve and area of a surface (see Chapter V). We shall define this generalized concept by taking as our definition an integral which (as I have said, for example, in sections 62 and 64) was often done for length and area. Examining this quickly, we shall also indicate another method of exposition, one that is well-known, that dispenses with the preliminary study of areas of order k that was made above in sections 97–100, and permits the immediate consideration of integration.

From a logical point of view, the preliminary study of areas that we made in the sections referred to served only for the concept of a quadrable domain. Now the definition of such a domain, since it depends only on the value of the area of order k of an interval (which can be assumed without explanation), could have been given without that study. From this we could have gone to the definition of an integral.

This being the case, the length of the segment $a \le x \le b$ being $\int_a^b dx$, let us call the expression $\int_\Delta dx_1\, dx_2$ the area of a quadrable domain Δ of the x_1x_2-plane and, more generally, let us call the expression $\int_\Delta dx_1\, dx_2 \ldots dx_k$ the area of order k of a quadrable domain in the space $x_1, x_2, \ldots, x_k$. The formula given in section 110 shows immediately that this area is independent of the rectangular coordinates chosen since, in the shift from one system of such coordinates to another, the functional determinant in question is ± 1.

Furthermore, for an interval one immediately finds the product of its dimensions. Therefore, the area of order k thus defined is an additive positive function, defined for quadrable domains of order k, that reduces to the product of the dimensions when the quadrable domain is an interval.

This establishes the identity of this concept with the concept of sections 97–100, if the latter has already been studied and, if not, makes it possible to get quickly to the facts shown in those sections.

This being the case, let us consider the k-dimensional manifold in n-dimensional space defined in rectangular coordinates by

$$I\begin{cases} X_i = F_i(u_1, u_2, \ldots, u_k); \\ i = 1, 2, \ldots, u. \end{cases}$$

This manifold is said to be linear if a change of rectangular coordinates in the n-dimensional space makes it possible to define it by the formulae

$$II \begin{cases} x_i = G_i(u_1, u_2, \ldots, u_k), & i = 1, 2, \ldots, k; \\ x_j = 0, & j = k + 1, \ldots, n. \end{cases}$$

A quadrable domain Δ_u in the space of the u corresponds on the linear manifold to the domain Δ, which we shall call quadrable of order k. We know (see section 110) that the family of these domains does not depend on the variables u chosen when we make only changes of variable of the type that we have been considering. To a domain Δ there corresponds in the space $x_1, \ldots, x_k$ a quadrable domain Δ_x.

If we had arrived at the canonical form II with the aid of other rectangular coordinates x' in the n-dimensional space, the orthogonality conditions of section 95 would have shown that the passage from x_1, $x_2, \ldots, x_k$ to $x'_1, x'_2, \ldots, x'_k$ is a change of rectangular coordinates in the k-dimensional space. Therefore, since the areas of order k are not altered by such changes, we shall speak of the *area of order k of a quadrable domain Δ of a k-dimensional linear manifold*. This will be the area of order k of Δ_x. Its value is

$$\int_{\Delta_x} dx_1 \, dx_2 \ldots dx_k = \int_{\Delta_u} \left| \frac{D(G_1, \ldots, G_k)}{D(u_1, \ldots, u_k)} \right| du_1 \, du_2 \ldots du_k.$$

This expression can also be written

$$\int_{\Delta_u} \sqrt{S \left\{ \frac{D(x_\alpha, \ldots, x_\lambda)}{D(u_1, \ldots, u_k)} \right\}^2} \, du_1 \, du_2 \ldots du_k,$$

where the sum S is all taken over all combinations of k subscripts $\alpha, \ldots, \lambda$ chosen from the sequence $1, 2, \ldots, n$. This is obvious since only one of these determinants is different from zero.

Now if we have

$$x_i = \alpha_i + \sum_{j=1}^{j=n} a_i^j X_j,$$

it follows that

$$\frac{D(x_\alpha, \ldots, x_\lambda)}{D(u_1, \ldots, u_k)} = S \left[\frac{D(F_{\alpha'}, \ldots, F_{\lambda'})}{D(u_1, \ldots, u_k)} \cdot \begin{vmatrix} a_\alpha^{\alpha'} & \cdots & a_\alpha^{\lambda'} \\ \cdots\cdots\cdots\cdots\cdots \\ \cdots\cdots\cdots\cdots\cdots \\ a_\lambda^{\alpha'} & \cdots & a_\lambda^{\lambda'} \end{vmatrix} \right],$$

where the symbol S denotes a summation over the combinations of primed indices.

From the orthogonality conditions, we derive by a classical procedure that

$$S \begin{vmatrix} a_\alpha^{\alpha'} & \cdots & a_\alpha^{\lambda'} \\ \cdots\cdots\cdots\cdots \\ a_\lambda^{\alpha'} & \cdots & a_\lambda^{\lambda'} \end{vmatrix}^2 = 1, \qquad S \begin{vmatrix} a_\alpha^{\alpha'} & \cdots & a_\alpha^{\lambda'} \\ \cdots\cdots\cdots\cdots \\ a_\lambda^{\alpha'} & \cdots & a_\lambda^{\lambda'} \end{vmatrix} \times \begin{vmatrix} a_\alpha^{\alpha''} & \cdots & a_\alpha^{\lambda''} \\ \cdots\cdots\cdots\cdots \\ a_\lambda^{\alpha''} & \cdots & a_\lambda^{\lambda''} \end{vmatrix} = 0,$$

where the first summation is taken over all the combinations $\alpha', \ldots, \lambda'$ and the second is taken over all pairs of different combinations $\alpha', \ldots, \lambda'$; $\alpha'', \ldots, \lambda''$.

We thus have $a_k(\Delta) = \displaystyle\int_{\Delta_u} \sqrt{S \left\{ \frac{D(x_\alpha, \ldots, x_\lambda)}{D(u_1, \ldots, u_k)} \right\}^2} \, du_1 \, du_2 \ldots du_k.$

Now that this formula is established for linear manifolds, the only ones for which $a_k(\Delta)$ is defined as yet, we shall take it as the definition for $a_k(\Delta)$ for *any* quadrable domain Δ of a k-dimensional manifold. The preceding calculation shows that this area is independent of the rectangular coordinates chosen, and it can easily be seen by generalizing the observations of section 83 that this area of order k is defined by conditions α, β, γ, and ϵ.

We might do over all of Chapter V, but I do not insist. *My purpose has been primarily to indicate a method of definition of a_k for domains in k-dimensional space different from the method presented in sections 97–100.*

In concluding this chapter, I feel that I should remind the reader that it would be completely inadmissible pedagogically to examine directly the general case with students and to bother with indices as was done above. My purpose in doing so was to shorten the work and yet to show that certain necessary precautions are too willingly forgotten, such as specifying the family of domains in question, and that people accept as evident and clear for n dimensions facts to which we are accustomed in dealing with only two or three dimensions.

VIII

CONCLUSIONS

The preceding chapters need no scientific or pedagogical conclusion. In no way do they seek to standardize instruction by representing some expositions as being better than the others. On the contrary, they seek to show the strong and weak points of each method of presenting the mathematical facts. The fact that it has seemed worthwhile to develop the less well-known procedures in greater detail does not in any way mean that they are to be preferred. In pointing out certain defects, errors, and gaps in the classical exposition, I did not at any time pretend to condemn them. On the contrary, I wish to help improve them. In my opinion, such a result could be obtained only by a critical comparative study of the various modes of exposition. I have tried to make such a study with regard to the measurement of magnitudes.

And if such studies are indeed indispensable for pedagogical progress (as I believe) and if they are necessary for choosing properly what one should say and knowing why one says it, they are thus an excellent pedagogical exercise that should be required of future teachers.

I said that at the beginning, and am returning to it now, because now I can explain better what I mean. The effort that I should like to see expected of future teachers differs from what is at present expected of them in that it does not propose to give them either a greater technical skill or philosophical learning.

As a rule, when one is dealing with the foundations of mathematics, it is the philosophical point of view that is taken. I have deliberately declined to do so, and some have seen in this attitude an indication of a scorn for philosophy.

This is not so. My good teacher, Jules Tannery, used to say, "It is prudent to respect, at least tentatively, what one does not know." Furthermore, ignorant as I am, I do not forget that it is because philosophers have meditated so long about problems (which are so difficult that one cannot even formulate them) that they succeeded in isolating the simpler questions, those with which the sciences deal.

We should respect philosophy. However, it does not follow that it can help us either to understand our sciences better or to advance them. It is a fact that the sciences have been primarily developed when they have become conscious of their individuality and have become separated from philosophy.

It is only natural and reasonable for the philosophers to test whether some method that has proven itself in the scientific domain might not be useful for them. This is going from the easy to the difficult. But that mathematics, which studies questions that are so simple that one can give precise and definitive solutions to them, should borrow from the resources of philosophy, which must content itself with imprecise and precarious answers, is something that I have not been able to admit.

Furthermore, all aspects of philosophical problems have been examined for centuries by men, some of whom have possessed genius. Would it not be an intolerable and, at the same time, naïve claim if a mathematician felt authorized to bring in his philosophical solutions because he has devoted some leisure time to meditation? By frankly admitting my incompetence, I believe that I am showing a much more genuinely sincere respect for philosophy.

In my opinion, a mathematician, as a mathematician, should not concern himself with philosophy, an opinion which, incidentally has been stated by many philosophers. His efforts at reflection and at comprehension should in some way be within the field of mathematics and not rest on the relationships between it and philosophy. True, the questions with which he has to deal do not possess either the same type of beauty or the poignancy of human interest that the philosophical problems possess. However, if one were to edify a philosophy of science for science's sake, this second-zone philosophy might possibly be the most effective aid for true philosophy.

The professor of mathematics, he too, should be able to limit the domain of his activity to what is objective. He is responsible for scientific culture; his philosophical colleague alone is responsible for philosophical culture.

In thus dealing exclusively with things that are in some way material and manual, we necessarily make mathematics a branch of physics. This branch is still differentiated from the others by the fact that in it we appeal to observation only in the beginning, in order to get our definitions and axioms. When a mathematician conceives, more or less clearly, a proposition instead of having recourse to experiment like the physicist, he seeks a logical proof. For him, logical verification replaces experimental verification. In short, he does not seek to rediscover but tries to become aware more clearly of the riches that he already unconsciously possesses in the definitions and axioms. Herein lies the supreme importance of these definitions and axioms, which are indeed subjected logically only to the condition that they be compatible but which would lead only to a purely formal science, void of meaning, if they had no relationship to reality.

The mathematics teacher, especially at the secondary level, does not need to develop pure logicians. He needs to help develop reasonable men, and, for that, he needs to deal not only with logical arguments but also with the acquisition of the premises of these arguments and the application of their results to the concrete. In the questions discussed in this book, I have not had much occasion to speak of this last point; it is none the less essential. By failing to show clearly the departure from the concrete and the return to the concrete, one risks having the students acquire a geometric mind in the derogatory sense of the term and to cause them to argue shamelessly from shaky data. The students must be taught to realize that nothing is demonstrated mathematically outside of mathematics, but that, nevertheless, logic is useful in all circumstances. Mathematics has been created by men to fill a need and it is indeed a valuable helper. The mathematics teacher should remain a teacher in action. It is not for him to raise philosophical doubt because, unlike his colleague in philosophy, he would not have the time nor the means to arouse and discipline it at the same time.

I do not believe it sufficient to require future teachers to have acquired technical skill and to be able to recite textbooks. We should require them to have thoroughly reflected about what they will have to teach in a spirit of logical and pedagogical criticism. We should require that they have made, either alone or helped by some instruction, a study on each main chapter analogous to the one that I have exhibited here on matters dealing with the measurement of magnitudes.

What lessons might future teachers draw from this study? First of all, it is certain that, to choose understandingly from the various expositions of the mathematical facts, it is necessary to have compared them and to have sought out their strong and their weak features and that, when this is done, one is then in a position to construct new ones if necessary. All that is quite clear. Let us pass to less obvious benefits. In examining arguments, if we see all the power of logic, we perceive also all its demands and we become conscious of the precautions that are necessary in applied mathematics.

In each chapter, I could have repeated what I said for arithmetic (see section 3): this chapter is applicable where it applies. Our absolute reasoning leads us in applications only to relative truths. There is always some disagreement between our logical premises and the reality that they propose to translate. For instance, we encountered the old question of irrational numbers. The ancients constructed by means of fractions a continuum that is completely sufficient for all human experiences no matter how great a degree of precision they may attain, but one that is logically insufficient. It was necessary (see sections 7 and 55) for us to extend the succession of measuring operations metaphysically in order to obtain a concept on which we can base a logical argument. To study the concrete or what seems concrete to us, we have had to make an expansion of what is real.

For the concept of area, the procedure used is in a way the opposite of that used for length, which I have just mentioned. In order to give area a logical basis, we confined ourselves to special domains, namely, the quadrable domains. Of course, in instruction intended for future teachers, one would have given, for example, proof of the existence of nonquadrable domains, which were here considered as just possible. Thus, we should exhibit a domain D such that, for any $\epsilon > 0$, two polygons differing from each other and from D by less than ϵ and possessing areas differing by an amount greater than an arbitrary prestated positive number can be exhibited. The physical concept of area is collapsing in a way. We have given up the idea of giving it a logical meaning in all cases. To give an area to D, it would be necessary to proceed to a new expansion of the concept of a number, just as was done in order to assign a length to the diagonal of the square constructed on the unit of length, and such an expansion would appear to us at first as being inadmissible and scandalous.

These statements would remind future teachers that mathematicians' efforts were made, in the beginning at least, to meet actual conditions, and they would be encouraged to speak of them. This would also show them all the resources that logic supplies to the intelligence and would show that, without intelligence, logic only leads to frustrations.

A physics teacher does not feel bound out of respect for experiment to conceal the intervention of intelligence in his physical researches. Too many mathematics teachers feel bound out of respect for logic to present mathematics as the inexorable unfolding of one and only one deductive path. If the names of certain mathematicians had not been associated, correctly or otherwise, with certain theorems, the pupils might forget that mathematics is only a human achievement. One never speaks of the choice of premises. One does not dare say that some proposition or other was obtained as a result of the *imaginative* qualities of a genius. We confuse the discovery of a proposition with the logical presentation made in the present-day manner. To listen to certain teachers, one would believe that Newton understood nothing about integration, that Euler was ignorant of series, and that Lagrange did not know what a function was. Everywhere, natural proofs are sought. Someone told me of a person who succeeded in finding, after six months of research, a natural proof that the three altitudes of a triangle meet in a single point. And people believe that by using natural proofs they are teaching the art of discovery.

If it were true that the method of rediscovery is the actual method of discovery, it would be known, for we are submerged under the discoveries of innumerable protagonists of rediscovery. Quite to the contrary, however, instruction based too systematically on rediscovery would actually be instruction in nondiscovery because, to discover something, it is necessary to make an unusual, *unnatural* approach, and the method of rediscovery consists in leading students towards certain catalogued arguments, always the same, and in teaching students to try them successively, without omission. It is true that this makes it possible to solve the problems because it is precisely problems amenable to this kind of reasoning that are proposed. But this taylorization of intellectual labor, this drilling, is quite different and is just the opposite of the flexibility that arouses the intelligence to discover new points of view.

Otherwise, the method of rediscovery is excellent. It has played the principal role in the transformation of mathematical instruction in the Lycées that has replaced the dreary classes of former days, when students played only a passive role, by the lively classes of today in which the students, in an active role, sense better the significance, the meaning, the interest, and the purpose of the propositions. It is also an excellent idea to use proofs showing the relation of the argument used to the types of arguments that are familiar to the students, and that are called natural for that reason. By feeling that they have been able to develop these proofs, the students understand them better and they acquire confidence in their own powers. But one should not expect of rediscovery or of natural proofs what they cannot give. They are excellent pedagogical techniques and nothing more. And these techniques would become harmful if they served to mask the role of intelligence or to suggest that working with mathematics is applying various sorts of rules to the letter.

Here are some questions of which one must necessarily think in the course of a critical study such as the one made here. It matters little to me whether the future teachers arrive at the conclusions that I have just formulated or at other conclusions. However, what I do wish is that they have a carefully thought-out opinion on points that are this fundamental.

Further, although I have just spoken of a critical study, have we actually made anything that merits the use of the word "critical" when, for example, in speaking of a whole number, we confined ourselves to describing the operation of numbering? Should we not have examined the concept of objects, of bodies that are being numbered? We have only indicated the arbitrariness of this concept, and this led us (see section 10) to multiplication. There is indeed more to be said. The concept of a body is clear only to one who is not critical of it. Physics is destroying it little by little. We have always known that the most highly polished solid body has rough outlines and pores and that in the cavities or in the material itself there are other bodies, impurities, liquids, gases. Then we learned that every solid bathes in an atmosphere of its own vapor that is always changing. Then the atomic theories concerning bodies, the planetary theories of atoms, render the concept of a body more and more uncertain. Is the division into bodies anything but a simplified construction of the world based on the notion of self, the only thing of which our primitive ancestors had a fairly clear conception? If the concept of a body has no absolute value, is not the concept of an integer, even the concept of the number *one*, the most false of all concepts? And what should we then say about the concept of a number in general, which we obtained only by replacing the vague concept of a body with the more intangible concept of a point?

It is clear that I am on a wrong path and that I have only cast the most sterile doubts by searching for the absolute when I was in the domain of the relative, and of gradations. A truly critical study of the concept of a body must be closely connected with an examination of our modes of thought when we strive to understand the world around us, and it would require us to leave the domain of mathematics. In saying this, I do not rule out going all the way to philosophical criticism, the interest and importance of which are in no way brought into question; but one would have to be able to devote a large amount of time to this to do it in a useful way and one would have to be prepared for it by previous studies. In addition to this criticism, there is another that is more within the field of mathematicians. This is the one that I have called logical and pedagogical criticism. It is the difference between this and purely philosophical criticism that I wished to point out.

Some famous and important works have shown the value of a more thorough study of elementary mathematics in relation to other branches of mathematics and to philosophy and history of science. I call attention to its pedagogical value.

Part II

DEVELOPMENT OF THE
INTEGRAL CONCEPT

Development of the Integral Concept is a translation by the editor of "Sur le développement de la notion d'intégrale," first published in *Matematisk Tidsskrift B*, 1926, reprinted in the *Revue de Métaphysique et de Morale*, 1927, and (in Spanish) in *Revista Matematica Hispano-Americana*, 1927.

THE DEVELOPMENT
OF THE INTEGRAL CONCEPT

Gentlemen:

Leaving aside all technicalities, we are going to examine the successive modifications and enrichments of the concept of the integral and the
appearance of other notions used in recent research on functions of a real
variable.

Before Cauchy there was no definition of the integral in the modern
meaning of the word "definition." One merely said which areas had to
be added or subtracted in order to obtain the integral $\int_a^b f(x)\,dx$.

For Cauchy a definition was necessary, because with him there
appeared the concern for rigor which is characteristic of modern mathematics. Cauchy defined continuous functions and their integrals in about
the same way as we do today. In order to arrive at the integral of $f(x)$
it suffices to form the sums (Fig. 1)

$$S = \Sigma f(\xi_i)(x_{i+1} - x_i), \tag{1}$$

which surveyors and mathematicians have always used to approximate
area, and then deduce the integral $\int_a^b f(x)\,dx$ by passage to the limit.

Although the legitimacy of such a passage to the limit was evident for
one who thought in terms of area, Cauchy had to demonstrate that S
actually tended to a limit in the conditions he considered. A similar necessity appears every time one replaces an experimental notion by a purely
logical definition. One should add that the interest of the defined object

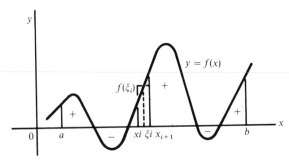

is no longer obvious, it can be developed only from a study of the properties following from the definition. This is the price of logical progress.

What Cauchy did is so substantial that it has a kind of philosophic sweep. It is often said that Descartes reduced geometry to algebra. I would say more willingly that by the use of coordinates he reduced all geometries to that of the straight line, and that the straight line, in giving us the notions of continuity and irrational number, has permitted algebra to attain its present scope.

In order to achieve the reduction of all geometries to that of the straight line, it was necessary to eliminate a certain number of concepts related to geometries of several dimensions such as the length of a curve, the area of a surface, and the volume of a body. The progress realized by Cauchy lies precisely here. After him, in order to complete the arithmetization of mathematics it was sufficient for the arithmeticians to construct the linear continuum from the natural numbers.

And now, should we limit ourselves to doing analysis? No. Certainly, everything that we do can be translated into arithmetical language, but if we renounce direct, geometrical, and intuitive views, if we are reduced to pure logic which does not permit a choice among things that are correct, then we would hardly think of many questions, and certain concepts, for example, most of the ideas that we are going to examine here today, would escape us completely.

For a long time certain discontinuous functions have been integrated. Cauchy's definition still applies to these integrals, but it is natural to examine, as did Riemann, the exact capacity of this definition.

If $\underline{f_i}$ and $\overline{f_i}$ represent the lower and upper bounds of $f(x)$ in (x_i, x_{i+1}), then S lies between

$$\underline{S} = \Sigma \underline{f_i}(x_{i+1} - x_i) \qquad \text{and} \qquad \overline{S} = \Sigma \overline{f_i}(x_{i+1} - x_i).$$

Riemann showed that for the definition of Cauchy to apply it is sufficient that

$$\overline{S} - \underline{S} = \Sigma(\overline{f_i} - \underline{f_i})(x_{i+1} - x_i)$$

tends toward zero for a particular sequence of partitions of the interval from a to b into smaller and smaller subdivisions (x_i, x_{i+1}). Darboux added that under the usual operation of passage to the limit $\underline{S}$ and $\overline{S}$ always give two definite numbers

$$\underline{\int_a^b} f(x)\, dx \qquad \text{and} \qquad \overline{\int_a^b} f(x)\, dx.$$

These numbers are generally different and are equal only when the Cauchy-Riemann integral exists.

From a logical point of view, these are very natural definitions, aren't they? However, one can say that from a practical point of view they have been useless. In particular, Riemann's definition has the drawback of applying only rarely and in a sense by chance.

It is evident that breaking up the interval (a, b) into smaller and smaller subintervals (x_i, x_{i+1}) makes the differences $\overline{f_i} - \underline{f_i}$ smaller and smaller if $f(x)$ is continuous, and that the continued refinement of the subdivision will make $\overline{S} - \underline{S}$ tend toward zero if there are only a few points of discontinuity. But we have no reason to hope that the same thing will happen for a function that is discontinuous everywhere. To take smaller intervals (x_i, x_{i+1}), that is to say values of $f(x)$ corresponding to values of x closer together, does not in any way guarantee that one takes values of $f(x)$ whose differences become smaller.

Let us be guided by the goal to be attained—to collect approximately equal values of $f(x)$. It is clear then that we must break up not (a, b), but the interval $(\underline{f}, \overline{f})$ bounded by the lower and upper bounds of $f(x)$ in (a, b). Let us do this with the aid of number y_i differing among themselves by less than ϵ. We are led to consider the values of $f(x)$ defined by

$$y_i \leq f(x) \leq y_{i+1}.$$

The corresponding values of x form a set E_i. In Figure 2 this set E_i consists of four intervals. With some continuous functions it might consist of an infinity of intervals. For an arbitrary function it might be very complicated. But this matters little. It is this set E_i which plays the role analogous to the interval (x_i, x_{i+1}) in the usual definition of the integral

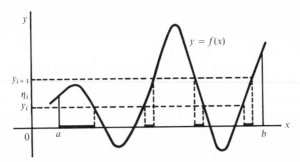

of continuous functions, since it tells us the values of x which give to $f(x)$ approximately equal values.

If η_i is any number whatever taken between y_i and y_{i+1}, $y_i \leq \eta_i \leq y_{i+1}$, the values of $f(x)$ for points of E_i differ from η_i by less than ϵ. The number η_i is going to play the role which $f(\xi_i)$ played in formula (1). As to the role of the length or measure $x_{i+1} - x_i$ of the interval (x_i, x_{i+1}), it will be played by a measure $m(E_i)$ which we shall assign to the set E_i in a moment. In this way we form the sum

$$S = \Sigma \eta_i m(E_i). \tag{2}$$

Let us look closely at what we have just done and, in order to understand it better, repeat it in other terms.

The geometers of the seventeenth century considered the integral of $f(x)$—the word "integral" had not been invented, but that does not matter—as the sum of an infinity of indivisibles, each of which was the ordinate, positive or negative, of $f(x)$. Very well! We have simply grouped together the indivisibles of comparable size. We have, as one says in algebra, collected similar terms. One could say that, according to Riemann's procedure, one tried to add the indivisibles by taking them in the order in which they were furnished by the variation in x, like an unsystematic merchant who counts coins and bills at random in the order in which they came to hand, while we operate like a methodical merchant who says:

I have $m(E_1)$ pennies which are worth $1 \cdot m(E_1)$,

I have $m(E_2)$ nickels worth $5 \cdot m(E_2)$,

I have $m(E_3)$ dimes worth $10 \cdot m(E_3)$, etc.

Altogether then I have

$$S = 1 \cdot m(E_1) + 2 \cdot m(E_2) + 5 \cdot m(E_3) + \cdots.$$

The two procedures will certainly lead the merchant to the same result because no matter how much money he has there is only a finite number of coins or bills to count. But for us who must add an infinite number of indivisibles the difference between the two methods is of capital importance.

We now consider the definition of the number $m(E_i)$ attached to E_i. The analogy of this measure to length, or even to a number of coins, leads us naturally to say that, in the example of Fig. 2, $m(E_i)$ will be the sum of the lengths of the four intervals that make up E_i, and that, in an example where E_i is formed from an infinity of intervals, $m(E_i)$ will be the sum of the length of all these intervals. In the general case it leads us to proceed as follows. Enclose E_i in a finite or denumerably infinite number of intervals, and let l_1, l_2, ... be the length of these intervals. We obviously wish to have

$$m(E_i) \leq l_1 + l_2 + \cdots.$$

If we look for the greatest lower bound of the second member for all possible systems of intervals that cover E_i, this bound will be an upper bound of $m(E_i)$. For this reason we represent it by $\overline{m(E_i)}$, and we have

$$m(E_i) \leq \overline{m(E_i)}. \tag{3}$$

If C is the set of points of the interval (a, b) that do not belong to E_i, we have similarly

$$m(C) \leq \overline{m(C)}.$$

Now we certainly wish to have

$$m(E_i) + m(C) = m[(a, b)] = b - a;$$

and hence we must have

$$m(E_i) \geq b - a - \overline{m(C)}. \tag{4}$$

The inequalities (3) and (4) give us upper and lower bounds for $m(E_i)$. One can easily see that these two inequalities are never contradictory. When the lower and upper bounds for E_i are equal, $m(E_i)$ is defined, and we say then that E_i is measurable.[1]

---

[1] The definition of measure of sets used here is that of C. Jordan, *Cours d'analyse de l'École Polytechnique*, Vol. I, but with this modification, essential for our purpose, that we enclose the set E_i to be measured in intervals whose number may be infinite, while Jordan employed only a finite number. This use of a denumerable infinity in place of a finite number of intervals was suggested by the work of Borel, who himself had utilized this idea in order to get a definition of measure (*Leçons sur la théorie des fonctions*).

A function $f(x)$ for which the sets E_i are measurable for all choices of y_i is called measurable. For such a function formula (2) defines a sum S. It is easy to prove that when the y_i vary so that ϵ tends toward zero, the S tend toward a definite limit which is, by definition,[2] $\int_a^b f(x)\, dx$.

This first extension of the notion of the definite integral led to many others. Let us suppose that it is a question of integrating a function $f(x, y)$ of two variables. Proceeding exactly as before, we construct sets E_i which are now sets of points in the plane and no longer on a line. To these sets we must now attribute a plane measure, and this measure is deduced from the area of rectangles

$$\alpha \leq x \leq \beta; \qquad \gamma \leq y \leq \delta$$

in exactly the same way as the linear measure was derived from the length of intervals. Once measure is defined, formula (2) gives the sums S from which the integral is obtained by passage to the limit. Hence the definition that we have considered extends immediately to functions of several variables.

Here is another extension which applies equally well regardless of the number of variables, but which I explain only in the case where it is a question of integrating $f(x)$ in the interval (a, b). I have said that it is a question of summing indivisibles represented by the various ordinates at points x, $y = f(x)$. A moment ago, we collected these indivisibles according to their sizes. Now let us merely group them according to their signs. We will have to consider then the set E_p of points in the plane whose ordinates are positive, and the set E_n of points whose ordinates are negative. As I recalled at the beginning of my lecture, for the simple case where $f(x)$ is continuous, even before Cauchy's time one wrote

$$\int_a^b f(x)\, dx = \text{area } (E_p) - \text{area } (E_n).$$

This leads us to assert

$$\int_a^b f(x)\, dx = m_s(E_p) - m_s(E_n),$$

where m_s stands for a plane measure. This new definition is equivalent to the preceding one. It brings us back to the intuitive method before Cauchy, but the definition of measure puts it on a solid logical foundation.

[2] *C.R. Acad. Sci. Paris*, **132**, 1900, pp. 1025–1028. Definitions equivalent to that given here have been proposed by various authors. The most interesting are due to W. H. Young, *Phil. Trans. Roy. Soc. London*, **204**, 1905, pp. 221–252, and *Proc. London Math. Soc.*, **9**, 1911, pp. 15–50. See also, for example, the notes of Borel and M. F. Riesz, *C.R. Acad. Sci. Paris*, **154**, 1912, pp. 413–415, 641–643.

We know now two ways of defining the integral of a function of one or several variables. And neither requires us to consider the more or less complicated form of the domain of integration because this domain enters only in the following way: the sets E_i in our first definition and the sets E_p and E_n in the second were formed by taking values of the function f only for points of the domain D.

Since the choice of domain of integration plays a role only in the formation of E_i, or of E_p and E_n, it is clear that we could as well form the sets E_i, E_n, E_p, by using the values of f at points of an arbitrary set E and in this way we could define the integral over any set.

In order to make precise the meaning of this new extension of the notion of integral, recall that our definitions required that f be measurable, that is to say that the E_i be measurable for the first definition and that E_p and E_n be measurable for the second, and that this required that E be measurable also. Hence we know how to define the integral over a measurable set of a function which is measurable and bounded on the set. I have up to now assumed implicitly that we are dealing with bounded functions.

What would have to be changed in the first manner of definition if the function to be integrated were not bounded? The interval $(\underline{f}, \overline{f})$ would no longer be finite. It would then require an infinity of numbers y_i to divide it into intervals of length at most equal to ϵ. There would be an infinity of sets E_i, and the sum S in formula (2) would now be a series. In order not to be stopped at the very beginning, we must suppose that the series S is convergent for the first choice of numbers y_i that we have to make. Now if S exists for one choice of y_i, it exists for all choices, and the definition of the integral applies without further modification.

The name of summable function has been given to all the functions which one can integrate by the indicated procedures, that is to say to all measurable functions for which the sum S has meaning. Every bounded measurable function is summable, and since no one has succeeded yet in naming a function that is not measurable,[3] one can say that up to the present practically all bounded functions have integrals. On the contrary, there exist very simple non-bounded functions that are not summable.

---

[3] Lebesgue did not admit the non-constructive methods by which non-measurable functions had been constructed before 1926, and a recent result of Robert Solovay (*Notices Am. Math. Soc.*, **12**, 1965, p. 217) shows that without such "inadmissible" procedures non-measurable functions cannot be defined. For an example of a non-measurable function, see Gelbaum and Olmsted, *Counterexamples in Analysis*, Holden-Day, San Francisco, 1964, p. 109—K.O.M.

Hence it is not surprising that our concept of the integral is still insufficient in certain situations.

We have extended the notion of integral to non-bounded functions by basing ourselves on the first of our definitions. The second definition leads to the same results. But for that it is necessary to enlarge the notion of measure so that it applies not only to bounded sets which we have considered up to now, but also to sets of points that extend to infinity. I mention this way of proceeding only because it is related to another extension of the integral in which the interval, the domain, the set over which the integral is taken, is no longer supposed finite, as we have up to now, but may go to infinity.

I limit myself to this passing mention because I will not discuss this extension further in this lecture. For the same reason I content myself with mentioning briefly the very original research undertaken by a young man killed in the war, R. Gateaux, who undertook to define the operation of integration for functions of an infinite number of variables. These researches, which were continued by Paul Lévy and by Norbert Wiener, are not unrelated to the axiomatic studies undertaken by M. Fréchet and by P. J. Daniell for the purpose of extending the integral concept to abstract sets.[4] Fréchet and Daniell not only proposed to apply to abstract sets the definitions that I have mentioned, but they considered also another extension of the definite integral to which we shall be led rather quickly by the notion of the indefinite integral, which we now examine.

One ordinarily considers the indefinite integral of a function $f(x)$ to be the function $F(x)$ defined by

$$F(x) = C + \int_a^b f(x)\, dx. \tag{5}$$

We do not follow this terminology, but instead give to the words "indefinite integral" their original meaning. Originally the two phrases "definite integral" and "indefinite integral" applied to the same expression $\int_a^b f(x)\, dx$.

The integral was called definite when it was a question of a given, determined, definite interval (a, b), and it was called indefinite when (a, b) was variable, not determined, and not definite, or if one wishes, indefinite.

[4] R. Gateaux, *Bull. Soc.Math. France*, **47**, 1919, pp. 47–96. P. Lévy, *Leçons d'Analyse fonctionnelle*, 1922. N. Wiener, *Proc. London Math. Soc.*, Ser. 2, **22**, 1922, pp. 454–467. M. Fréchet, *Bull. Soc. Math. France*, **43**, 1915, pp. 248–265. P. J. Daniell, *Ann. of Math.*, Ser. 2, **20**, 1919, pp. 281–288.

Indeed it is by a real abuse of language that one calls $F(x)$ the indefinite integral of $f(x)$. If we note in addition that when one studies $F(x)$ it is always in order to obtain properties of $\int_a^b f(x)\,dx$, that basically it is $\int_a^b f(x)\,dx$ that one studies by means of $F(x)$, one will be led to say: define the indefinite integral of $f(x)$ as the function $\Phi(a, b)$

$$\Phi(a, b) = \int_a^b f(x)\,dx = F(b) - F(a). \tag{5'}$$

Between an indefinite integral and the corresponding definite integral there is the same relation and the same differences as between a function and a particular value taken by the function. If we represent by D the interval (a, b) of integration, we can say that the indefinite integral is a function whose argument is the domain D,

$$\Psi(D) = \Phi(a, b).$$

From these considerations it clearly results that for a function of two variables one should not take for the indefinite integral, as is sometimes done, the function

$$F(X, Y) = c_1(x) + c_2(y) + \int_\alpha^X \int_\beta^Y f(x, y)\,dx\,dy. \tag{6}$$

If one considers only rectangular domains $a \le x \le b$; $c \le y \le d$, one must take for the indefinite integral the function of four variables

$$\Phi(a, b; c, d) = F(b, d) + F(a, c) - F(a, d) - F(b, c). \tag{7}$$

But since the most general domain cannot be determined by a finite number of parameters, if we wish to consider all domains of integration, we must give up ordinary functions in order to represent the correspondence between a domain D and the integral over this domain and instead study directly the function

$$\Psi(D) = \iint_D f(x, y)\,dx\,dy,$$

whose argument D is a domain. It is this function that we call the indefinite integral of $f(x, y)$. Or rather, since we have defined the integral of f over a measurable set E, we consider the indefinite integral as a function of sets which will be defined for all measurable sets.[5]

What has been said so far is only a matter of language, of names, but these questions of terminology would not come up if we had not acquired a new idea. It is for this reason that one should not be surprised that the new language has enabled us to perceive the full significance of facts

[5] *Ann. Sci. École Normale Supérieure*, Ser. 3, **27**, 1910, pp. 361–450.

observed first in connection with the function $F(x)$ in formula (5). In particular, we have succeeded in characterizing the set functions that are indefinite integrals by two properties: complete additivity and absolute continuity.[6]

When a set function $\Psi(E)$ has these two properties it is the indefinite integral of a function which depends on 1, 2, 3, . . . variables according to whether the sets E are formed from points of a line, plane, ordinary space, etc. In order to have a uniform language and notation we say that f is a point function, $f(P)$, and we write

$$\Psi(E) = \int_E f(P)\, dm(E). \tag{8}$$

The function $f(P)$ is entirely determined by $\Psi(E)$, to the extent that one can modify f arbitrarily at points of an arbitrary set of measure zero without $\Psi(E)$ ceasing to be its indefinite integral. And one can obtain $f(P)$ from $\Psi(E)$, except for a set of measure zero, by the following procedure.

Let P be the point in which one wishes to calculate f. Take for domain of integration Δ an interval of center P, or a circle of center P, or a sphere of center P, . . . , according to whether we are dealing with the line, plane, or space, . . . , and form the ratio $\Psi(\Delta)/m(\Delta)$. Then let Δ tend to zero and we have

$$\lim_{\Delta \to 0} \frac{\Psi(\Delta)}{m(\Delta)} = f(P). \tag{9}$$

This result obviously generalizes the classic theorem according to which if $f(x)$ is continuous, the function $F(x)$ in the formula (5) has f for derivative. Indeed our procedure for calculating $f(P)$ is a sort of differentiation of the set function $\Psi(E)$.

This kind of differentiation was considered long ago. Cauchy[7] uses the term "coexistent quantities" to refer to quantities determined at the same time, that is to say by the same conditions. If, for example, one has a body that is non-homogeneous in composition and density, and if one

---

[6] These terms are due respectively to de La Valée-Poussin, *Intégral de Lebesgue, Fonctions d'ensemble, Classes de Baire*, Paris, 1916, and to G. Vitali, *Atti R. Acc. Sci. Torino*, **43**, 1908, pp. 229–246.

A measurable set function $\Psi(E)$ is completely additive if, in whatever way one divides E into a finite or denumerable number of pairwise disjoint measurable sets $E_1, E_2, \ldots$, one has $\Psi(E) = \Psi(E_1) + \Psi(E_2) + \cdots$.

A measurable set function $\Psi(E)$ is absolutely continuous if, when E varies in such a way that $m(E)$ tends to zero, $\Psi(E)$ also tends to zero.

[7] *Exercices d'analyse et de physique mathématique*, Paris, 1840–1847, Vol. 2, pp. 188–229.

considers a domain D of this body, the volume of D, the mass of D, the quantity of heat necessary in order to raise by one degree the temperature of D supposed isolated, are all co-existent quantities. They are functions $V(D)$, $M(D)$, $Q(D)$ of the domain.

It is no accident that we arrive here at functions of domains. If one thinks about it, one quickly sees that all physical magnitudes are related not to points but to extended bodies and are therefore functions of domains, at least in so far as they are directly measurable magnitudes. The body to be considered is not always a body of our space of experience. It may be a body in a space of purely mathematical conception if in the determination of the considered magnitude there intervene non-spatial variables like time, temperature, etc. But that makes little difference. Directly measurable magnitudes, such as mass, quantity of heat, quantity of electricity, for example, are functions of domains and not point functions.

However, physics also considers magnitudes attached to points, such as speed, pressure, density, specific heat. But these are derivative magnitudes which one ordinarily and correctly defines by the ratio or the limit of the ratio of two coexistent magnitudes, for example,

$$\text{density} = \frac{\text{mass}}{\text{volume}}, \quad \text{specific heat} = \frac{\text{quantity of heat}}{\text{mass}}.$$

That is to say, one takes the derivative of a quantity with respect to a coexistent quantity.

Thus, physics, and in consequence geometry, leads to the consideration of functions of a domain and to their differentiation just as does the analysis of functions of real variables. It is even true that functions of domains play in some sense a more basic role in physics than do point functions. Why then do the physicists not speak of these functions? Because mathematicians have as yet not studied them and because algebra does not have a notation for either the domains or the functions of domains. Therefore, one sees the physicist limit himself to considering special domains depending only on certain parameters, so that the function of a domain is reduced to a function of parameters. But this is exactly what the mathematician does when, instead of considering the definite integral of $f(x, y)$ in all its generality, he limits himself to considering the functions $F(x, y)$, $\Phi(a, b; c, d)$ of formulae (6) and (7).

We notice that formula (8) establishes a connection between the set functions $\Psi(E)$, which are indefinite integrals, and the point functions

$f(P)$, which are amenable to algebra. This formula (8) furnishes then a sort of notation for certain set functions. Now if we examine the two conditions required for a function to be an indefinite integral, we cannot doubt that the functions of physics are among the domain functions susceptible of being indicated by this notation.

These reflections on the nature of physical magnitudes may have enabled you to understand more precisely the interest and the significance of the ideas that we have discussed. They show, in particular, that the operation of differentiation which appears in formula (9) is not the only one to consider. One could always consider the differentiation of a function $\Psi(x)$ with respect to a coexistent function $p(E)$, whether or not this function was the measure $m(E)$.

Now another question quickly comes to mind. Could one also replace the function $m(E)$ by a given function $p(E)$ in the definition of the integral? There is no difficulty in doing so. First of all, we replace formula (2) by $S = \Sigma \mu_i p(E_i)$. This requires first that the sets E_i belong to the family of those for which the function $p(E)$ is defined—that is to say that the function to be integrated must be measurable with respect to $p(E)$. Second, the series S must be convergent—that is to say, f must be summable with respect to $p(E)$. Under these conditions, the integral of $f(P)$ with respect to $p(E)$,

$$\int f(P)\, dp(E),$$

will be defined as before if the function $p(E)$ possesses a certain property which one expresses by saying that $p(E)$ must be of bounded variation.[8]

We have just arrived at a new and very substantial extension of the notion of the integral by taking the formal point of view of a mathematician. The point of view of the physicist leads even more naturally to the same result, at least for continuous function $f(P)$. One could even

---

[8] $p(E)$ is said to be of bounded variation if, when one subdivides E into a denumerable set of pairwise disjoint subsets $E_1, E_2, \ldots$, the series $\Sigma |p(E_i)|$ is convergent. The notion of function of bounded variation was first introduced by C. Jordan in relation to a function of one variable. The only set functions $p(E)$ that are considered in these theories are additive functions, that is to say, those for which one has $p(E_1 + E_2 + \cdots) = p(E_1) + p(E_2) + \cdots$, with the $E_1, E_2, \ldots$ being pairwise disjoint. If additivity is complete, that is to say, if the sequence of $E_1, E_2, \ldots$ may be taken arbitrarily, $p(E)$ is necessarily of bounded variation. For if the order of the sets E_1, $E_2, \ldots$ is indifferent, the series $p(E_1) + p(E_2) + \cdots$ must remain convergent regardless of the order, that is to say, the series $\Sigma |p(E_i)|$ is convergent. So far no effort has been made to eliminate the condition that $p(E)$ be of bounded variation. It is necessary to remark, however, that if $p(E)$ is not of bounded variation, one can find a function $f(P)$ which is continuous and to which our definition of the integral does not apply.

say that physicists have never considered anything else but integrations with respect to functions of domains.

Suppose, for example, that one wishes to calculate the quantity of heat, $\varphi(D)$ necessary in order to raise by one degree the temperature of the body D of which we spoke above. It is necessary to divide D into small partial bodies D_1, D_2, . . . of masses $M(D_1)$, $M(D_2)$, . . . , to take in each one of them a point, P_1, P_2, . . . , and to take for the approximate value of $\varphi(D)$ the sum $f(P_1)M(D_1) + f(P_2)M(D_2) + \ldots$, where $f(P)$ represents the specific heat at P. This means that we are calculating $\varphi(D)$ by the formula $\varphi(D) = \int_D f(P) \, dM(E)$.

In its general form the new integral was first defined in 1913 by Radon. It was known since 1894 for the particular case of a continuous function of one variable, but its original inventor, Stieltjes, was led to it by researches in analysis and theory of number and he presented it in a purely analytical form which masked its physical significance, so much so that it required much effort to understand and recognize what is nowadays obvious. The history of these efforts includes the work of F. Riesz, H. Lebesgue, W. H. Young, M. Fréchet, and C. de La Vallée-Poussin. It shows that we were rivals in ingenuity, in insight, but also in blindness.[9]

And yet mathematicians were always considering integrals of the Stieltjes–Radon type. The curvilinear integral

$$\int_C f(x, y) \, dx$$

is one of these integrals, where the function $p(E)$ is defined in terms of the length of the projection on the x-axis of arcs of C. The integral

$$\iint_S f(x, y, z) \, dx \, dy$$

in the same way involves a set function defined in terms of the areas of S projected on the xy-plane.

In truth these integrals most often appear in groups

$$\int_C f(x, y) \, dx + g(x, y) \, dy,$$

$$\iint_S f(x, y, z) \, dx \, dy + g(x, y, z) \, dy \, dz + h(x, y, z) \, dz \, dx.$$

[9] J. Radon, *Math.-Nat. Kl. Sitz. Kais. Ak. Wiss. Vienna*, **122**, Pt. IIa, 1913, pp. 1295–1438. T. J. Stieltjes, *Ann. Fac. Sci. Univ. Toulouse*, **8**, 1894, pp. J68–J122. F. Riesz, *C. R. Acad. Sci. Paris*, **149**, 1910, pp. 974–977. H. Lebesgue, *C. R. Acad. Sci. Paris*, **150**, 1910, pp. 86–88. W. H. Young, *Proc. London Math. Soc.*, **12**, 1913, pp. 41–88. M. Fréchet, *Nouv. Ann. des Math.*, Ser. 4, **10**, 1910, pp. 241–256. C. de La Vallée-Poussin, *op. cit.*

If one considers also the integrals used for the definition of lengths of curves or areas of surfaces,

$$\int_C [dx^2 + dy^2 + dy^2]^{1/2}, \qquad \iint_S [(dx\,dy)^2 + (dy\,dz)^2 + (dz\,dx)^2]^{1/2},$$

one will be led to say that it would be convenient also to study methods of integration in which there appear several set functions $p_1(E)$, $p_2(E)$, ... Such a study is entirely for the future although Hellinger and Toeplitz have utilized certain summations with respect to several set functions.[10]

So far we have considered integration, definite or indefinite, as an operation furnishing a number, definite or variable, by a sort of generalized addition. We have taken the point of view of quadratures. But we can also look upon the integration of a continuous function as yielding a function as in the simplest integration of differential equations. This is the point of view of primitive functions which we will now consider.

To look for the primitive function $F(x)$ of a given function $f(x)$ is to find the function, determined up to an additive constant when it exists, which has $f(x)$ for derivative. It is this problem that we are going to study.

But we note that the preceding discussion leads to the formulation of the problem in a much more general way. Given a function $f(P)$ which is the derivative with respect to a known function $p(E)$ of an unknown function $\Psi(E)$ to find the primitive function $\Psi(E)$ of $f(P)$.

If, for example, we have a continuous function $f(x)$ and a measure $m(E)$, the primitive function will no longer be the function $F(x)$ of formula (5) but the indefinite integral

$$\int_E f(x)\,dx.$$

I can only mention this general problem which has not yet been studied. I will limit myself to saying that the Stieltjes integral is quite insufficient for its solution. In fact, this integral has been defined only under the hypothesis that $p(E)$ is a bounded variation, and one can quite well speak of the derivative with respect to a function $p(E)$ of non-bounded variation.

The theory of summable functions furnishes the following result in

---

[10] See, for example, *J. reine angew. Math.*, **144**, 1914, pp. 212–238.

case $p(E)$ is the measure $m(E)$: when the derivative $f(P)$ is summable, the anti-derivative of f is one of its primitive functions. I say one of the primitive functions because we do not yet know how the general problem of primitive functions should be stated so as to be determinate.[11]

Let us leave these questions, of which I have spoken only in order to indicate how much remains to be done, and let us show how much has been done in the search for the primitive function $F(x)$ of $f(x)$, thanks above all to Arnaud Denjoy.

I have just said that when $f(x)$ is summable, integration gives $F(x)$ by formula (5). Let us suppose that in (a, b) $f(x)$ ceases to be summable only at a single point c. In that case integration gives $F(x)$ in $(a, c - \epsilon)$, for arbitrarily small ϵ and hence for all (a, c). It also furnishes $F(x)$ in $(c + \epsilon, b)$, and hence in all (c, b). And taking account of the continuity of $F(x)$ at the point c, we have $F(x)$ in the entire interval (a, b). By such considerations of continuity,[12] one sees that if one knows $F(x)$ in every interval that contains no point of a set E in its interior or at its extremities, one can, by an operation which I call A, determine $F(x)$ on every interval contiguous to E, that is to say, on every interval with end points in E but having no interior points in E.

Suppose now that one knows $F(x)$ in the intervals (α, β) contiguous to a set E, that the sum $\Sigma[F(\beta) - F(\alpha)]$ is convergent, and that $f(x)$ is summable on E.[13] Then it suffices to say that the primitive function must result from the contribution of E and intervals contiguous to E in order to be led to the formula

$$F(x) - F(a) = \left\{ \int_E f\,dx + \Sigma[F(\beta) - F(\alpha)] \right\}_a^x.$$

The braces indicate that one must utilize only points between a and x. From this formula there results the determination of $F(x)$ by an operation which I call B.

The two preceding results mark the extreme points to which I came in my thesis, and I must say that I indicated them only as it were by

[11] In this connection see the notes by Fubini and Vitali, *R. Acc. Sci. Torino*, **50**, 1915, pp. 293–296; **51**, 1916, pp. 143–147 and *Atti Rend. R. Acc. Lincei*, **24**, 1915, pp. 691–693; **25**, 1916, pp. 684–688.

[12] It is the introduction of these conditions of continuity that distinguishes substantially the problem of primitive functions from that of quadratures.

[13] It is appropriate to notice that these hypotheses are not contradictory even if E is supposed to be the set of points of non-summability of $f(x)$ in the interval (a, b). In order to determine the points of non-summability in (a,b) it is necessary to take account of all the points of (a, b), whether they belong to E or not, whereas the summability on E is a condition which involves only the points of E.

chance, for I had no idea of the importance that would be given to them by Denjoy.

Relying on the results of Baire, Denjoy showed that if $f(x)$ is a derivative function on (a, b), then

1. The points where $f(x)$ is not summable form a set E_1 non-dense on (a, b). An operation O_1 of type A determines $F(x)$ on intervals contiguous to E_1.

2. Hence there exists a set E_2, formed of points of E_1 and non-dense on E_1 in whose contiguous intervals one can calculate $F(x)$ by an operation O_2 of type B.

3. Hence there exists a set E_3, formed of points of E_2, in whose contiguous intervals one can calculate $F(x)$ by an operation O_3 of type B. . . .

If after an infinite sequence of operation O_1, O_2, . . . one has not yet found $F(x)$ on the entire interval (a, b), the points of (a, b) which are not interior to intervals in which one has found $F(x)$ form a set E, and an operation of type A, the operation O_ω, gives F in the intervals contiguous to E_ω. One considers then, if it is necessary, operations $O_{\omega+1}$, $O_{\omega+2}$, . . . of type B, then an operation $O_{2\omega}$ of type A, then operations of type B, etc.

And Denjoy, utilizing now classical arguments of Cantor and Bendixson, proved that this procedure finally gives us $F(x)$ in all of (a, b) after a finite or denumerable sequence of operations.

This procedure, certainly complicated but in principle as natural as those previously considered, was called totalization by Denjoy.

Totalization resolves completely the problem of finding the primitive function $F(x)$ of a given function $f(x)$. It even permits one to find $F(x)$ when one knows only a derivate[14] of $f(x)$ and not its derivative. I will not dwell on these beautiful results. The most important fact for us is that totalization, by a long detour, furnishes us a new extension of the notion of the definite integral. In fact whenever totalization applies to a function $f(x)$ and makes correspond to it a function $F(x)$, we can attach to $f(x)$ an integral thanks to formulae (5) and (5').[15]

[14] Or "derived number," that is, any of the four upper or lower derivatives from the left or right—K.O.M.

[15] Denjoy, *Annales sc. de l'Ecole normale supérieure*, **33**, 1916, pp. 127–222 and other papers 1915–1917 in this journal, *Journal de Math.* and in *Bull. Soc. Math. France*. A student of Denjoy, H. Looman, has studied (*Fundamenta Mathematicae*, **4**, 1923, pp. 246–285) how one may find a function $F(x, y)$ knowing $f(x, y) = F''_{xy}(x, y)$. This problem is closely related to the search for a set function $\Psi(E)$ whose derivative with respect to $m(E)$ is $f(x, y)$.

And now, gentlemen, I pause to thank you for your kind attention and to offer a final word of conclusion, if you will permit. It is that a generalization made not for the vain pleasure of generalizing but in order to solve previously existing problems is always a fruitful generalization. This is proved abundantly by the variety of applications of the ideas that we have just examined.